Doug Pratt's Modeling Guides

Learn to Fly
RC Helicopters

Dale Hart

TAB TAB BOOKS
Blue Ridge Summit, PA

FIRST EDITION
FIRST PRINTING

© 1991 by **TAB Books**.
TAB Books is a division of McGraw-Hill, Inc.

Library of Congress Cataloging-in-Publication Data

Hart, Dale.
    Learn to fly RC helicopters / by Dale Hart.
       p.   cm.
    Includes index.
    ISBN 0-8306-3619-6 (paper)
      1. Helicopters—Models—Radio control.   I. Title.
TL776.H37   1991
629.133'1352—dc20   91-11178
                                  CIP

TAB Books offers software for sale. For information and a catalog, please contact
TAB Software Department, Blue Ridge Summit, PA 17294-0850.

Acquisitions Editor: Jeff Worsinger
Book Editor: April D. Nolan
Production: Katherine G. Brown
Book Design: Jaclyn J. Boone

Contents

Introduction

*T*ransmitter on . . . check. Receiver on . . . check. Verify controls . . . check. Attach glo-driver . . . check. Add throttle trim . . . check. Apply starter and depress starter switch.

The engine turns over and comes to life. You remove the starter and adjust the throttle trim for a smooth idle. Now you remove the glo-driver and are pleased to see that the engine is still running. You move back from the bird and check the air traffic—all clear. As you ease the throttle up, the engine responds smoothly. Almost at half-stick, the heli gets light on her skids. Half-stick, and she's in the air!

You carefully hover her while the engine comes up to operating temperature. Check the blade tracking while maintaining a motionless hover at an altitude of five feet. Add tail rotor to slowly pirouette your pride and joy a full 360 degrees, all the while checking out her controls. Satisfied, you point her nose downwind and increase throttle to gain speed and altitude. She responds instantly and quickly races away. As she gains altitude and speed, you flick on hi idle 1. Now you turn 180 degrees and bring her around, nose into the wind. At an altitude of 100 feet, you ease back on the throttle and fly her with the cyclic. She sounds sweet as she flies past, so you turn her around and bring her by again. The heli still sounds good, so you flick on hi idle 2 and do a roll. Ah, that felt good!

Turn 180 degrees and bring her by once again. On this pass you decide to perform an Immelmann. Easing the collective back, you enter a climb. Going halfway through, you roll out, working the collective to minimize the drag created by the rotor blades. On the next pass you decide to do a Split-S. Here she comes, nose level. Right cyclic and decrease collective . . . inverted. Push forward on the cyclic, diving. Hold forward cyclic, add collective, add throttle, nose level, and fly through!

OK, let's have some real fun, you say. Let's try that again, but this time let's tie it all together—roll, Immelmann, Split-S. Let's add a loop, now a stall turn—but make it with a half-roll on the way up. Exit the maneuver flying at high speed downwind. Set up for an autorotation landing from an altitude of 250 feet, flick on the throttle hold, and guide her down, adding a 180-degree turn near the bottom to land nose into the wind, six feet in front of you!

Nothing compares to flying an RC helicopter. Ask anyone who has been at it for some time, and they will fill your ears with the most remarkable flying stories you've ever heard. It's a bug that bites hard and doesn't let go easily. Most modelers are very passionate about their hobby, but not everyone takes to rotary-winged flight! You are interested in pursuing the hobby; that's why you are reading and researching the subject. Maybe you are already into RC aircraft and are looking for another challenge, or maybe you're a novice to the hobby. Whatever the reason, welcome to a most fascinating aspect of model aviation.

Chapter **1**

Getting
started

*T*his chapter will give you a quick idea of what
it takes to get involved in the hobby of RC helicopter flying. In later chapters, I will go into greater detail, explaining each of the components of the
helicopter.

KIT TYPES

Several types of model helicopters are available these days, but the most
common type are "kits." A kit is a box of machined parts and fasteners
with illustrated drawings and building instructions (FIG. 1-1). In addition,
modern technology has given birth to the Almost-Ready-to-Fly (ARF) kits.

1-1 The Kyosho Concept 30 DX kit shown here represents a typical kit. Parts are
packaged by assembly steps, and an instruction manual is included.

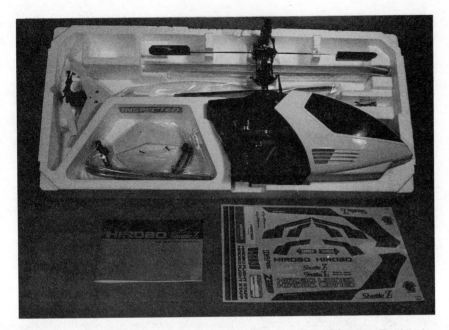

I-2   Some helicopter kits are available in Almost-Ready-to-Fly (ARF) form. The Hirobo Shuttle ZX is typical, with 90% of the assembly completed at the factory.

These are becoming more popular, and their name aptly describes the amount of assembly required (FIG. 1-2).

Kits require more time and dedication to realize the finished product, but they do have their advantages. Although you must be fairly handy with tools and able to follow mechanical drawings to complete a kit successfully, it's not as complicated as it might seem. With each kit you receive a set of written instructions as well as full mechanical drawings or plans of the model. Most manufacturers have taken great pains to make assembly as easy as possible, so the drawings usually have exploded views of the subassembly and/or the entire model (FIG. 1-3). Each step of the assembly is numbered in sequence, and the parts are separately bagged and numbered to correspond to the step.

The instructions often refer to specific views on the drawings to clarify a step. It might take some time in the beginning to get used to the sequence, but once you get the hang of it, assembly goes quite smoothly. Approximate assembly time is typically around 40 hours.

Putting a kit together takes some of the mystery out of the model and acquaints you, the builder, with common helicopter terminology. It also makes repairing your model easier.

ARFs, on the other hand, come with the majority of the work already completed. After some minor assembly, all you need to do is to install the radio and engine (and some ARFs even come with the engine already mounted). ARFs commonly employ extensive use of high-tech plastics to keep replacement costs down. In many cases, the inherent flexibility of

1-3 The instructions for the GMP Rebel are typical of what is found in most kits. Drawings are used to show the assembly steps.

the plastic also helps minimize crash damage. ARFs take much less time to complete than kits, usually between 1 to 10 hours. While ARFs come with instruction manuals to aid the assembly, most do not include mechanical drawings.

The easiest kits to assemble are those based on ARF models. These feature the assembly methods and materials that make factory assembly practical, so you can expect to complete the model in less time than the more sophisticated kits require. An added bonus to such kits is the lower purchase price—and, of course, the experience you gain by doing more of the work yourself.

Whether you choose to complete a kit or an ARF model, you'll need some tools (FIG. 1-4). If you have been involved with RC modeling, you should already have the basics. If this is your first endeavor, you will need a small screwdriver set, a small wrench set, and allen keys (if they are not included with the kit). Most helicopters use metric sizes, so keep that in mind as you purchase tools. You just need the basics at first; other specialty tools can be purchased at a later date.

ENGINES

The typical model helicopter is powered by a 2-cycle glow engine. Glow engines have been popular for many years in other forms of radio control modeling, because of their simple design. Glow engines also put out high power for their weight and size.

The size of the engine is determined by the model you choose. Engines range in size from .10 to .80 cubic inches, with the most popular

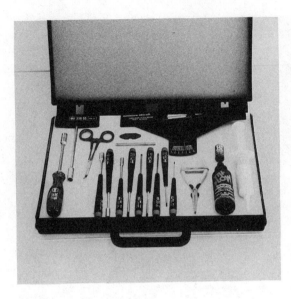

1-4 This tool kit from Miniature Aircraft USA, or one like it, will provide you with the most common specialty tools that you will need. Tools can also be purchased individually.

sizes being between .32 and .60. A mixture consisting mainly of methanol and oil is used for fuel instead of gasoline. This allows you to use a glow plug for ignition rather than a spark plug, which would require an electrical system. The glow plug must be powered by a 1.5-volt external battery during the starting procedure. Once the engine is running, glow is maintained by the heat of combustion, and the battery is no longer needed.

STARTING EQUIPMENT

You'll need several pieces of equipment to get your helicopter in the air. To start the engine, you will need a power source for the glow plug. While your power source can be as simple as a large 1.5-volt dry-cell battery, several options are available. Power panels will provide power to the glow plug, as will rechargeable glow-plug igniters. A hand-held starter powered by a 12-volt battery is normally used to spin the engine while starting. A 5-amp motorcycle battery is a convenient way to power the starter, but a car battery can also be used. As an alternative, some helicopters can be fitted with a pull-start system similar to that used on a lawn mower.

RADIO EQUIPMENT

The helicopter is controlled by a remote control system that transmits radio signals to a receiver in the model (FIG. 1-5). The receiver relays the appropriate information to each of the control servos. A *servo* is a small device powered by an internal electric motor. A feedback device helps control the exact position of the external control arm.

Each function on the helicopter is mechanically connected to its own servo. The typical helicopter will have either four or five servos. Power for the airborne system is supplied by a 4.8-volt rechargeable battery pack, while the transmitter is powered by a separate 9.6-volt rechargeable

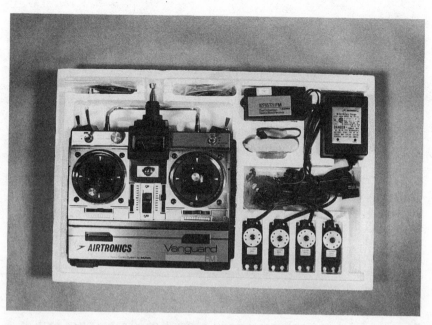

1-5 You'll need a radio control system to operate your new helicopter. This Airtronics Vanguard system is a typical beginner's radio.

battery pack. The batteries and charger are included with practically all radios on the market. Anywhere from three to five servos are included with a radio, but you can buy additional servos separately.

A *gyroscopic stabilizer* is a highly recommended optional component that can be added to the airborne flight system. A gyro helps control unwanted rotational movement of the model, and it is much faster and more sensitive when making corrections than you, the pilot, can be. For this reason, using a gyro allows you to concentrate on the rest of the controls while the gyro controls the model rotation. A gyro is most beneficial during the learning stages, but even experienced pilots prefer to use one.

HOBBY SHOPS AND CLUBS

If you are lucky enough to have a hobby shop nearby, it is an ideal place to start looking for the items you'll need. Some hobby stores carry only one or two types of equipment, while others specialize in model helicopters and their supplies. Check the telephone directory to find out if the shop is helicopter-oriented before you start out.

Even if your local hobby shop does not stock helicopter kits, they should be able to order what you want. Any shop that sells RC airplanes is a good place to get some of the extra items you will need, such as starting equipment and fuel.

Another avenue to consider for purchasing equipment is the mail-order house. Several large companies carry products for all aspects of the RC hobby, including helicopters. Before you order, however, you must know exactly what you want. Some hobby shops specializing in helicopters will ship mail orders, and these stores will usually provide more assistance in making selections. Many times the person answering the phone at a smaller shop will be an accomplished helicopter pilot. You will find a variation in prices between the different outlets, but you should consider the amount of assistance offered when deciding where to buy your equipment. It's hard to put a price on good advice.

Clubs are formed by modelers with the same interests to offer their members benefits like obtaining a flying site, fellowship at monthly meetings, and assistance in learning how to fly. Some clubs have members involved in many aspects of the RC hobby, while other clubs specialize in only one aspect. Your local hobby shop will know if there are any clubs in your area and what their interests are. Finding a club with helicopter pilots will give you a chance to get help and advice while learning and will add to your enjoyment of the hobby. Even if there are no clubs locally, inquiring at the nearest hobby shop might give you the opportunity to meet other helicopter enthusiasts.

FLYING SITES

Once you have your helicopter ready, you will need a safe place to fly it. A level area free of obstructions (such as trees) will be needed. For the initial flights, an area at least 50 feet square is suitable, but try to find a larger area, if possible, so you'll have more room for the helicopter to drift as you learn the controls.

Pavement or short grass works well because these surfaces allow the helicopter to move about on its training gear. Tall grass and weeds should be avoided. Such surfaces can cause the helicopter to tip if it is moving sideways while landing. Smooth surfaces, on the other hand, allow the helicopter to slide without tipping over during landing.

As you gain experience you will need a larger area to practice moving the helicopter about. Once you advance to fast-forward flying, you'll need a much larger area. Joining a club might be the best way to find such a site (FIG. 1-6).

NATIONAL ORGANIZATIONS

The Academy of Model Aeronautics (AMA) is the governing body for all facets of model aviation. As such, the AMA provides the modeler with up-to-date information on each subject on a monthly basis. Also included with the membership is liability insurance. For this reason, most clubs require AMA membership before joining the club.

The AMA publishes a set of rules for competition including the required maneuvers for each skill level. The Academy also provides recommendations for flying sites, a safety code, and a sense of unity among all modelers.

The International Radio Controlled Helicopter Association (IRCHA) is a special interest group dedicated to helicopters. The IRCHA is recognized

1-6 A suitable flying site for your new helicopter will have plenty of open area and a smooth surface. Joining a model aircraft club is one way to obtain a safe flying site.

by the AMA as such and has a large input on rules and general guidelines for helicopters. A membership in IRCHA offers the member newsletters containing all the latest advances, helicopter tips, and a calendar of upcoming events throughout the country.

If you'd like more information, you'll find the addresses of these organizations at the end of this book.

Chapter 2

Helicopter basics

*T*he traditional fixed-wing aircraft receives its lift from air flowing over the wing. To cause this airflow, there must be a certain amount of forward speed, which is normally generated by the thrust of a propeller or a jet engine. The blades on a helicopter are similar to the wings of an aircraft, but instead of having the wing fixed in a stationary position and moving the entire craft, a helicopter uses the power of the engine to rotate the blades fast enough to create lift. By removing the need to propel the entire aircraft, a helicopter gains the ability to maintain altitude without moving, to move sideways, and even to move backwards. A whole new realm of flight is possible.

The blades on a helicopter are mounted to the *rotor head*, which supports and controls the blades. The rotor head is, in turn, mounted to the main shaft. The power of the engine is transferred through the transmission to the main shaft, which spins the rotor head and its blades, creating the lift needed to support the helicopter.

A side effect of using the engine to turn the main rotor is the torque reaction that is generated. The drag of the blades and gearing cause the helicopter body to rotate in the opposite direction of the main rotor—an effect that must be counteracted in some way to prevent the helicopter from spinning uncontrollably. Adding a smaller rotor system to the tail of the helicopter solves the problem. The tail rotor is driven by the same engine and adjusted to produce the exact amount of thrust required to balance the torque.

Once the lift has been achieved, it must be controlled. If the amount of lift is equal to the weight of the helicopter, the craft will neither climb nor descend. If the lift is greater than the weight, the helicopter will climb; if the lift generated is less than the weight of the helicopter, it will descend. In a collective pitch system, the angle of attack of the blades is changed to control lift. On a fixed pitch system, the rotor speed is increased or decreased.

9

ROTOR BLADE PITCH CONTROL

RC helicopters offer two different types of rotor blade pitch control systems, fixed pitch and collective pitch. The following are brief explanations of each, but I will go into greater detail in chapter 3 when I discuss radio systems and their advantages and disadvantages.

Fixed pitch

With a fixed pitch system, all vertical movement of the helicopter is controlled by varying the speed of the engine with the throttle, which in turn increases or decreases the speed of the rotor system. As the rotor speed changes, the amount of lift created also changes, causing the model to rise or descend. While this does make for a very simple method of controlling the rotor thrust, there is one major drawback. Because it takes time to change the speed of the rotor blades, there is a noticeable lag in control response. With a lot of practice, though, the pilot can learn to anticipate this delay and make allowances for it (FIG. 2-1).

2-1   A fixed pitch rotor head, as seen on this GMP Rebel, is the ultimate in simplicity. Altitude is controlled by varying the speed of the rotor head.

Collective pitch

Its name sounds confusing, but in reality the collective pitch is the most common form of lift control. The name *collective pitch*, put simply, means that the pitch of both blades is changed together, or collectively, by coordinating several controls to produce the desired effect (FIG. 2-2).

2-2 Collective pitch rotor heads, such as the one on this Kyosho Concept 30, offer precise altitude control. The angle of both blades can be changed to rise or descend on command.

With a helicopter radio, some of the control functions are electronically mixed.

The following is a typical scenario. As you raise the throttle stick, the angle of the main rotor blades increases. At this point, more power is necessary to maintain rotor speed, so either through mechanical linkages or a mixing circuit in the radio, the carburetor is opened further. This continues until full pitch and full power have been reached.

Once torque is applied against the body of the helicopter, the tail rotor mixing circuit comes into play. This circuit increases the pitch of the tail rotor blades to compensate for the added torque. The helicopter will now stay pointed in the right direction. Remember, when the lift created is greater than the weight, the helicopter will become airborne!

FLYBAR

The *flybar* is a metal rod with control paddles on each end. It is mounted above, in line with, or below the main rotor blades at a perpendicular angle.

On a model helicopter, the flybar acts as a stabilizer for the helicopter, adding corrections to compensate for sudden fore, aft, or sideways movements. However, the flybar is not capable of sensing the slow drifting movement of a helicopter.

On a collective pitch rotor head, the flybar is used to amplify the control inputs made by the pilot. On a fixed pitch helicopter, however, the flybar is the only means of controlling the rotor head.

When a control input tilts the swashplate, the *pushrod* connected from the swashplate to the flybar control arm causes the flybar to twist as the rotor goes around. The paddles attached to each end of the flybar change their angle of attack, causing one side of the flybar to be pulled up while the other side is pushed down. On a fixed pitch helicopter, the flybar and rotor hub are mounted so that they tilt together. On a collective pitch helicopter, the flybar tilts by itself, while the control arm or arms attached to the flybar move pushrods connected to the mixing arms. The mixing arms then combine the inputs coming directly from the swashplate with those coming from the flybar and change the pitch of each blade accordingly.

SWASHPLATE

The *swashplate* is comprised of two rings joined by a ball bearing. The lower ring does not rotate, but the upper one does because it is coupled to the main rotor. The swashplate is mounted so that it can be tilted by control rods connected to the lower ring. The upper ring then passes these control inputs on to the rotor head (FIG. 2-3).

2-3 A typical swashplate consists of two rings joined by a ball bearing. Control rods fastened to the lower ring tilt the swashplate in the desired direction. As the upper ring rotates, it passes the control inputs on to the rotor head.

The swashplate is situated on the main shaft, directly above the frame of the helicopter. Before reaching the rotor head, all of the cyclic control functions—fore/aft and left/right tilting of the model—must first pass through the swashplate. To move the model in any direction, the corresponding control tilts the swashplate accordingly. In effect, then, the swashplate controls the direction of the model.

For example, in a left lateral move, as viewed from the tail of the helicopter, the swashplate would tilt downward on the left side. To move forward, the *front* of the swashplate would dip down.

On a collective pitch system, control rods connecting the swashplate to the rotor head relay the control inputs to the individual blades as they go around. On a fixed pitch system, a single rod is connected from the swashplate to the flybar. As the rotor head goes around, inputs from the swashplate are passed on to the flybar. As the flybar tilts, so does the rotor head, effectively increasing pitch on one blade while decreasing pitch on the other.

In a typical collective system using a flybar, the control rods travel through a set of mixing arms before reaching the blades. The swashplate may also be used to change collective pitch. On a sliding swashplate model, the entire swashplate moves up and down to add or subtract pitch (*angle of attack*) in order to increase or decrease the altitude of the model. Other models employ a control rod through the main shaft for the same effect.

TAIL ROTOR

The *tail rotor* has a function similar to the collective pitch system's. A control arm changes the pitch of both tail blades to produce the correct amount of thrust according to command input. The pilot can control the *yaw* (rotational) movement of the helicopter. In forward flight, the tail rotor acts very much like the rudder on an airplane, pointing the nose in the proper direction. When a helicopter is hovering, you can use tail rotor control to rotate the helicopter.

Control inputs from the tail rotor servo are transferred to the pushrod fastened to the tailboom, through the bellcrank, to the sliding ring. As the ring moves in or out on the output shaft, the angle of the tail blade changes. This varies the amount of thrust produced, causing the helicopter to rotate left or right (FIG. 2-4).

The tail rotor blades start out with a positive angle of attack, usually 8 to 10 degrees, at hover. This is used to counteract the torque created by powering the main rotor blades. To change the heading you, the pilot, would increase or decrease the attack angle.

The tail rotor is sometimes part of the electronic mixing circuits of the radio system. This feature is found only in model helicopter radios and, while it's not mandatory, it can be a considerable help to the beginning pilot. Without this special circuit, you have to compensate for the increased torque created by the helicopter as it lifts up and begins to hover. You must make a control input to increase tail blade pitch while simultaneously increasing throttle—regardless of whether you choose a fixed or collective pitch helicopter.

BLADES

All helicopters rely on the spinning mass above their craft to create motion, so they all need rotor blades. All kits contain a set of blades ready to cover and mount, and ARF kits usually include prefinished blades. Most

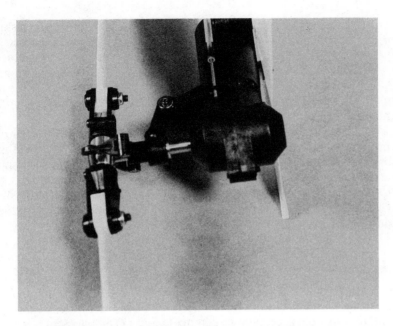

2-4 Control inputs from the tail rotor servo are transferred from the pushrod fastened to the tailboom, through the bellcrank, to the sliding ring. As the ring moves in or out on the output shaft, the angle of the tail blades changes. This varies the amount of thrust produced, causing the helicopter to rotate left or right. This Kalt Enforcer tail rotor assembly is a typical one.

blades are made of wood, but some are constructed with foam and fiberglass.

If you inspect high-quality wood blades closely, you will see that they are made of different materials. The fat or *leading edge* is usually made of a hard wood, while the thin edge or *trailing edge* is composed of softer wood, usually balsa. The blades are constructed this way for a very good reason. I won't bore you by going off on a physics tangent. In basic terms, the lighter material on the trailing edge improves the *chordwise* or front-to-back balance point, which should be located as close as possible to the pivot point of the blade.

Several types of airfoils are used on blades, but the most common one is symmetrical. As viewed from the tip, fully symmetrical blades have the same shape on both sides (FIG. 2-5), while semi-symmetrical blades usually have a curved top and a fairly flat bottom. Semi-symmetrical blades create more lift during normal flying than do symmetrical blades. However, during aerobatics with inverted portions, symmetrical blades are equally efficient both inverted and upright.

Weighted blades maintain their inertia much longer than unweighted blades. The extra weight aids the flywheel effect of the rotor system, which is beneficial for hovering as well as during an engine-off landing, or *autorotation* (FIG. 2-6). The weight of the blades is a storage point for kinetic energy, which supplies the continued rotor speed while the heli-

2-5 The fully symmetrical airfoil is visible on the end view of these blades, installed on a Schluter Junior 50.

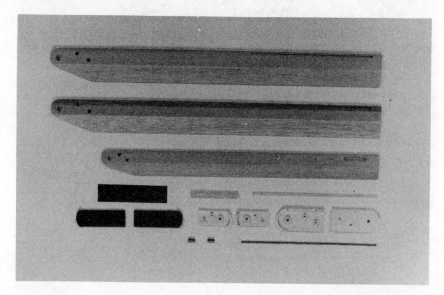

2-6 These RotorSport wooden blades, from Miniature Aircraft USA, are available in different sizes to match the size of the helicopter.

copter gently descends. Using weighted blades certainly has its benefits, but they are not necessary for a beginner.

Plastic or foam composite blades offer light weight as well as a corrected center of gravity. These CG-corrected blades are equally suited for aerobatics and for introduction flights. Such blades are not as durable as wood blades, but they come ready to bolt onto the model, so no extra work needs to be done before you attach them. Fiberglass blades are also CG corrected and can be configured with or without added weight, but fiberglass is quite expensive. You can't buy a mass-produced kit that supplies fiberglass blades, but you can purchase them later, when you have reached the point in your hobby where you can take advantage of their benefits.

POWER TRAIN

The *power train* on a model helicopter is very much like that on a full-scale helicopter, having four major components to it. First is the motor. Its job is obvious—without it, you'd have a gliding stone! As the motor revs up, the centrifugal clutch engages, transferring the power to the main gear (FIG. 2-7).

2-7 A common drive train layout is found in this Schluter Champion helicopter. The main gear (right) is driven by the pinion gear (left), which is fastened to the clutch bell housing. A centrifugal clutch is incorporated to facilitate engine starting.

The main gear is connected to the rotor system and the tail rotor drive system. Tail rotor drive can be accomplished by a shaft, a wire, or a belt. As the motor speed increases, so does the speed of the other components. Normally the motor will turn eight to ten times for every one turn of the main gear. The tail rotor drive will turn four to six revolutions for every main rotor revolution.

ENGINES

The most popular engine used to power an RC helicopter is a two-cycle glow engine, the same kind of engine that has been used for many years in other forms of RC modeling. The 2-cycle engine does not have intake and exhaust valves like other engines. Instead, the movement of the piston opens and closes ports cut in the side of the cylinder wall to allow the fuel/air mixture to enter and the exhaust to exit. The elimination of the traditional valve train significantly reduces the number of parts in the engine.

Since a model 2-cycle engine uses an alcohol-based fuel, the spark plug and related electrical system is replaced with a simple glow plug. The glow plug resembles a miniature spark plug on the outside, but inside the electrode is replaced by a thin coil of special alloy wire. When you apply voltage, the wire will glow, allowing the engine to be started. Once the engine is running, the electrical power is no longer necessary. The heat of combustion will keep the glow plug hot enough to ignite the next fuel charge in the cylinder (FIG. 2-8).

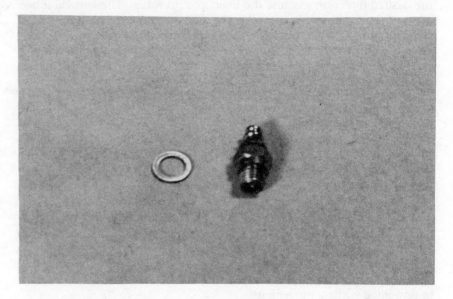

2-8 Two-cycle glow engines, as used in model helicopters, are equipped with a glow plug to make ignition possible. A 1.5-volt power source is used to heat the wire during engine starting. After that, the heat of combustion keeps the glow plug lit.

Glow plugs come in a variety of heat ranges and styles. Usually, the higher the number, the colder the heat range of the plug. The middle of the range is a good place to start.

Both long and short style plugs are available, but only the smallest engines use short plugs. Check the engine instructions to be sure, but most likely you will need a long plug.

Glow plugs are available with and without *idle-bars*. The idle-bar plug was designed to improve the idle on some engine designs, but there is a slight power loss that accompanies the idle bar design. Consult specific engine instructions for more suggestions.

TRANSMITTERS

The transmitter is your link to controlling the model helicopter. As you move the control sticks, a signal sent from the transmitter to the receiver relays the information to the model. The most common type of transmitter has two control sticks, each being able to move up, down, left, and right. Most pilots hold the transmitter in both hands, using their thumbs to control the sticks, but others prefer to hold the control sticks between their thumbs and forefingers. You can also use a neck strap to help hold the radio. (These are often included with the radio.)

An alternative to the dual-stick radio is the less popular single stick. With this type of radio, a single, dual-axis control stick has a knob mounted on top of it that controls the yaw of the model. Therein lies the single-stick radio's main advantage: The pilot simply twists the knob in the desired direction to cause the helicopter to rotate. The vertical movement of the helicopter is controlled by a lever on the right side or top of the transmitter. Cradle the single-stick transmitter in your left hand, using your thumb or forefinger to control the throttle. Holding the knob in your right hand, you have control of the fore/aft, left/right, and rotation movements of the helicopter.

Most transmitters operate on the 72 (megahertz) MHz band. Channels have been assigned by the FCC strictly for model aircraft use. For ease of identification, these channels have been numbered, ranging from 12 to 56. Only one model may operate at a time on an individual channel. For this reason, organized flying sites use a frequency-control system, which can be as simple as a board with a separate clothespin for each channel. Before turning on a transmitter in such a situation, a pilot must obtain the proper pin.

You can find radio systems that use either amplitude (AM) or frequency modulation (FM). As you would expect, the FM systems tend to be more reliable—just as a car radio receives more static on AM than on FM, so does the RC system. AM systems are affected more by the noise caused by metal-to-metal contact on the helicopter. This problem results in unwanted control movements.

While FM is more resistant to the problems that affect AM systems, the very best radio systems use something called Pulse Code Modulation (PCM). A normal radio transmits pulses to signify the position of each control, but in a PCM radio, these pulses are converted into a code that is transmitted. The receiver sends the signal to a decoder that converts the signal back to pulses, giving the receiver the ability to recognize noise in the form of bad signals and ignore it, retaining the last good control signal it received. PCM systems eliminate many forms of interference, but cannot be expected to cope with another radio on the same channel.

RECEIVERS

The receiver is the most important airborne component of the radio system. Obviously, it must receive the signal from your transmitter but while doing so, it also has to ignore all other signals that are present. Many of these signals are stronger than those sent by the transmitter. Fortunately, the receivers currently on the market are extremely reliable under most conditions. Local clubs or hobby shops should be able to advise you if you should avoid certain channels in your area.

The receiver must be of the same design as the transmitter, whether AM, FM, or PCM. Additionally, both transmitter and receiver must be on the same channel. When purchasing a complete system, this is no problem because manufacturers package all the proper components in one box (FIG. 2-9).

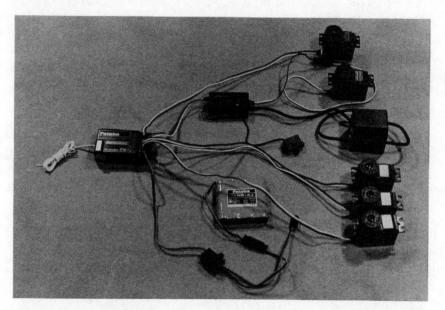

2-9 A complete flight pack consists of the receiver, five servos, a gyro, the switch harness, and a battery pack.

The best PCM receivers have additional features such as *fail-safe* and *hold*. Typically, this type of receiver will use the hold function for the first one second of strong interference. During this time, all controls remain at their last position, ignoring the bad information being received. If the interference continues for more than one second, then fail-safe takes over. Fail-safe causes each control to go to a preselected position until the interference ends. Normally the controls will be set to go to neutral and the engine to go to idle, in order to minimize the damage in case of a crash.

By having the controls go to neutral, it might be easier to recover if control is regained before the model reaches the ground.

Also found on PCM receivers is a low-voltage warning. If the airborne battery pack goes below a certain voltage, the receiver warns you by reducing the throttle to approximately the one-quarter position. Pulling the throttle stick all the way back briefly gives you full throttle control again long enough to land the helicopter. This system works quite well with airplanes, but might not work so well with helicopters because the pitch is controlled by the same stick as the throttle. Your natural tendency when you see the helicopter drop would be to increase throttle, which would cause the rotor speed to drop if the engine is not delivering normal power. By the time you realize what the problem is, it might be too late.

SERVOS

The servos provide the muscle to move each control to the desired position. Through the receiver, each individual servo is sent a signal telling it where the servo arm should be. A *feedback potentiometer* inside the servo is connected to the output shaft, which holds the servo arm. Then the electronics in the servo compares the present position of the servo arm to the signal it has just received. If the servo arm is not in the right position, the motor is turned on in the direction needed to move the servo arm to the new position. When the feedback pot tells the servo that it is in the right position, the motor shuts off.

Each radio manufacturer makes several models of servos. The differences lie in the size, power, and precision of the servo. The least expensive radio systems come with the base model servo, which should be quite adequate when learning. Higher-quality servos can be substituted either when buying a radio or through a separate purchase at a later date. The benefits of higher-quality servos become more apparent on larger helicopters. As the size of the helicopter increases, so does the demand placed on the servos. The additional power and speed available make the controls more responsive.

To increase durability, it is common for the higher-quality servos to use ball bearings to support the output shaft. This helps handle the sideways load placed on the servo output shaft.

As the old adage says, don't let size fool you. Neither the smallest nor the largest servo is necessarily the best. As the quality of the servo increases above that of the base model, the size often decreases because of the use of smaller, more efficient, but more expensive components. As further gains in power are made, the size of the servo may increase again. You have to look at all the specifications of an individual servo before making a decision on which one to purchase. Radio manufacturers generally designate one of their best servos as the recommended choice for helicopters, and these will be included with the top-of-the-line systems.

GYROSCOPIC STABILIZER

A *gyroscopic stabilizer* (gyro) is a device that connects between the receiver and the tail rotor servo. Control inputs from the pilot's receiver are passed through the gyro directly to the servo. The gyro senses even the slightest rotational movement of the helicopter and sends a signal to the servo to make the proper correction (FIG. 2-10). The amount of correction is proportional to the speed at which the helicopter is rotating. The

2-10 This Futaba G-154 gyroscopic stabilizer shows the correct procedure for plugging the wires in. Control signals from the pilot are sent from the receiver (left) through the gyro (center) to the servo (right). Any corrections the gyro senses are needed then are added to the signal being sent to the servo.

pilot can make the same corrections as the gyro, but not as quickly. Mounted directly on the helicopter, the gyro senses movement before you are able to notice it. By allowing the gyro to make many of the small tail rotor corrections, you can concentrate on the other controls.

The typical gyro consists of several parts connected by cables. A small, square box houses the gyro motor and sensor. The motor is mounted on bearings that allow it to rock side to side. On each end of the motor shaft is a small flywheel. When the gyro motor is running, rotating the gyro housing causes the motor to tip sideways. The sensor detects the amount and direction of movement and relays this information to the control box and the necessary control input is passed on to the servo (FIG. 2-11).

2-11 With the cover removed from this Airtronics gyro sensor, the inner workings are revealed. A small motor spins the brass flywheels that are located on each end. As the helicopter rotates, the motor/flywheel assembly tips to one side. The electronic circuit senses this and sends the appropriate correction to the servo.

Signals from the receiver are passed directly through the control box. Located on the control box are one or more *control pots* or switches. The sensitivity adjustment controls how strong a correction is made for a certain amount of helicopter movement. When this is set as low as possible, the gyro will have no effect. If it is set too high, the gyro will overcompensate, causing the model to yaw back and forth continuously. The ideal setting will vary with an individual pilot's skill level and the maneuvers he is performing.

More advanced gyros allow you to adjust the sensitivity of the gyro from the transmitter, either in the form of a two-position switch selecting which setting on the gyro to use, or a knob on the transmitter that proportionally adjusts the sensitivity.

Most gyros also have a direction switch on the control box, which is used to set the direction of compensation. It is similar to servo reversing, but affects only the gyro inputs, not those coming from the pilot. It is very important to set the direction switch correctly; having it set wrong is worse than having no gyro at all. Some gyros also have a neutral adjustment that works the same as the rudder trim on the transmitter, but has a larger effect.

Top-of-the-line gyros offer the option of using a separate power supply for the gyro motor. A voltage regulator in the control box keeps the voltage consistent. By isolating and regulating the power to the gyro motor, consistent rpm is gained. This prevents any change of gyro sensitivity from beginning to end of a flight. A side benefit is that the separate power supply reduces the load on the main battery pack.

BATTERIES

Most RC modelers use rechargeable batteries, commonly called *NiCad* batteries. These differ from alkaline batteries in that they give you a relatively constant voltage to the point of depletion, where they drop suddenly to almost no voltage.

NiCad batteries are rated in milliamps (mA) with ratings such as 500 mA or 1200 mA. The receiver pack is a group of four cells ranging in size from AA to Sub C size. The higher the rating, the longer the pack will last. Using a typical five-channel system with a gyroscopic stabilizer, a recommended minimum capacity pack would be 1000 mA, which would give you about 1 1/2 hours of safe flying time. Remember that any time you have the system on, it counts towards your actual flight time.

The individual cells have a 1.2-volt capacity and are wired in series to give you 4.8 volts. The transmitter uses a battery pack consisting of eight cells, producing 9.6 volts. A gyro's power comes from the flight pack or an additional battery pack. The more sophisticated gyros are capable of using a second battery pack, in which case the gyro will accept 6 volts coming from a NiCad pack consisting of five cells. Should you decide to use separate packs, two 500-mA packs are sufficient—one each for servo control and the gyro. If a single pack is used for both, then a larger pack is in order; in this case, I highly recommend you use a 1000-mA or 1200-mA pack. Unfortunately, some radio systems only come with a 500-mA pack. A larger pack can be purchased separately or the individual cells can be purchased and put together to achieve the desired size.

CHARGERS

If NiCad batteries are used in the radio (which is standard practice), then the radio system will include battery chargers for both the transmitter and receiver packs. These can be plugged in and left on for up to three days without over-charging the batteries, and they require a minimum of 16 hours to charge fully.

Several brands of chargers offered by other companies have unique features, including multiple charging, quick charging, and automatic switching to trickle charging when the normal charging cycle has been completed. While such features are nice to have, they are not necessary and can be added at a later date.

CONTROL MOVEMENTS

The most fascinating aspect of helicopter flight is the ability of the aircraft to move in any direction or in no direction at all. It can sit still in a hover, or move front, back, left, or right. It can rotate around its axis over one spot on the ground, or combine several movements at once. Once moving forward, the helicopter can bank onto its side and make a smooth turn. It can descend smoothly to a desired spot, ending its descent in a stationary hover.

Typically, the model helicopter is controlled by a transmitter with two control sticks. Each stick moves both up/down and left/right. There are several control arrangements that are used, but the most common is called Mode II, and this is the method I will describe throughout this book. Let's start by taking a look at how the transmitter's control stick movements relate to the helicopter movements.

The left stick on the transmitter is used to control climb/descent and rotation of the helicopter. With the control stick pulled toward the bottom of the case, the engine will be at idle; this is where it should be while starting the engine. Once you are ready to lift the model off the ground, pushing the left stick forward will cause the model to climb. At approximately the middle stick position, the lift created by the helicopter will be equal to its weight. At this point, the model will maintain its altitude, neither climbing nor descending. Moving the stick above the halfway point will cause the model to climb. With the stick pushed all the way forward, full power will be used to climb as quickly as possible.

Pulling the stick below the halfway point will cause the helicopter to develop less lift than what is required to support its weight, allowing the helicopter to drop or descend. Pulling the stick all the way back will cause the model to descend as quickly as it can.

The left stick also moves sideways. This control is used to rotate the helicopter. A spring inside the transmitter causes the stick to return to neutral as soon as it is released. As the stick is pushed to the left, the front of the helicopter will move to the left. As the stick is pushed to the right, the nose of the helicopter will move to the right. The further the stick is moved away from neutral, the faster the helicopter will rotate.

Some people hook up this control to respond in the opposite direction so that they can watch the tail of the helicopter and control it by moving the stick the same direction as they want the tail to move. This may work well while learning to hover, but will not be as easy when you are ready to start moving the helicopter through a turn. With the normal control setup, to make the helicopter turn to left during forward flight, you push the stick to the left. When the control is set up to fly the tail, it becomes necessary to push the stick to the right to make a left turn, which could be confusing. So unless you have an instructor who suggests otherwise, it's best to use the normal control setup.

On the right side of the transmitter is another stick. This one has a pair of springs that centers the stick in both axes and controls the tilt of the helicopter. As you push the stick forward, the nose of the model will drop. If you leave the stick in this position, the helicopter will move forward. Pulling the stick back toward the pilot raises the nose of the helicopter, stopping any forward movement and causing the model to go backwards. Moving the stick to the left makes the model tilt to the left, and moving the stick to the right makes the model tilt to the right. You can also move the right control stick diagonally to achieve a combination of movements.

Keeping the helicopter in a stationary hover requires small but frequent control movements. You'll need to make corrections for slight changes in wind direction and speed. You can also deliberately move the helicopter in any direction by tilting it slightly. To stop the movement, tilt it the other way, then level it before the model starts moving in the new direction. As the speed of the model increases, the control reactions will be slightly different.

In a hover, pulling the right stick back will raise the nose and lower the tail, making the model move backwards. When the helicopter is in forward flight, pulling the stick back will still raise the nose, but the forward momentum will allow the model to climb for a while before losing speed. If the helicopter is going fast enough, holding the stick back will allow the model to do a loop.

In a similar way, moving the right stick sideways will cause the helicopter to lean in the same direction. If the helicopter is moving slowly, it will slip in the direction it is leaning. If it is flying at full speed, holding the stick hard to one side will cause the helicopter to do a roll. Negative pitch should be used while the helicopter is upside down, but that will be explained in a later chapter.

Chapter **3**

Choosing equipment

*Y*ou must make quite a few choices when getting started in the hobby of RC helicopters. Most important is choosing the proper equipment to suit your requirements. This chapter will offer advice in choosing your first helicopter and the related products. Later, in chapter 8, I will review some of the most popular helicopters and radios currently on the market.

SIZE RANGES

The first item to discuss is the size of the helicopter, which is usually defined by the recommended engine size. The smallest size engine is the .25 to .32 (cubic inch) range, the middle size is the .40 to .50 range, and the largest common size is the .60. A comparison of two models with different sized engines is shown in FIG. 3-1. Let's start by looking at some of the advantages and disadvantages of each size.

The .25- to .32-size helicopter is the smallest of the three common sizes. The most obvious advantage is the lower cost of purchasing the helicopter kit and maintaining it (commonly known as putting the darn thing back together). In addition, this size range offers several different models that can be purchased as fully assembled models. The high quality and performance of kits in the smaller range has made them one of the most popular sizes.

The main disadvantage of the .25- to .30-range models is the small size itself. The smaller a model helicopter is, the more it is affected by the wind. Therefore, the smaller size and inherent lighter weight of the small models make them very susceptible to wind. Visibility is also not as good with the smaller models as it is with the larger ones.

The largest common model helicopter size is the .60, and this is practically the only size used in competition. But the same things that make the .60 the most competitive also can make it the easiest to fly. The increased weights of the airframe, blades, and stabilizer paddles act

3-1   A Kyosho Concept .30 is shown here in front of a Schluter Champion (.60 powered) for size comparison.

together to improve the feeling of stability. Visibility is much improved over the smaller chopper (which will help when you let the helicopter get too far away from you). Also, the quality of the parts and the number of ball bearings used in the kit generally increases with the size range. The only disadvantage is that an increased price accompanies the increased quality.

The last size range to consider is the .40 to .50 size. As you would expect, this size of model has some of the advantages and disadvantages of its smaller and larger brothers. It can also be a very nice compromise.

Most helicopters in this size range use many parts from the larger models from which they are derived, but leave out some of the expensive but nonessential parts. The side frames and tailboom are usually smaller and lighter in .40-to-.50-size heli. You might choose to replace some of the bushings with bearings at a later date, but such performance improvements are not necessary for the novice pilot.

Even an advanced sport pilot should not overlook the mid-size helicopter. While this size helicopter can easily be over two pounds lighter than a .60, a .50 engine will put out almost as much power, providing the experienced pilot with a helicopter that has spectacular vertical performance, agility, and a physical size large enough to make high-speed forward flight comfortable for greater distances.

FIXED PITCH vs. COLLECTIVE PITCH

The next thing to consider when choosing a helicopter is what type of rotor blade pitch control system you want. As you recall, chapter 2 discussed the mechanics of the fixed pitch and collective pitch systems. Now let's look at the advantages and disadvantages of each.

Besides the simplicity of the fixed pitch system, one of its main benefits is its low cost. A fixed pitch system also uses less parts in the rotor system and is suitable for using a four-channel "aircraft" radio system rather than a "helicopter" radio (see the end of this chapter for more details).

While the fixed pitch system is the most basic system in use, few models employ its use because of its limitations. Because the fixed pitch system uses throttle to control lift, a considerable lag in response occurs. The pilot must anticipate what control inputs will be needed and adjust accordingly. Another major disadvantage of the fixed pitch system is that *autorotation* is not available. Autorotation allows you to land the helicopter safely should the motor quit—certainly an important feature.

The collective pitch system is by far the most common type found on model helicopters in the past five to ten years. Although it is a more complicated system, its fast, precise control response makes it much easier for the model to start or stop climbing or descending—and this is very helpful when trying to keep the model in a stationary hover. In addition, autorotation is available in collective pitch systems and, as I mentioned, this is an attractive advantage that could prevent serious damage to your model should the motor quit in flight.

A "helicopter" radio will let you fully appreciate the advantages of a collective pitch control system, but a four-channel radio can still be used successfully by combining the throttle and collective pitch functions onto one servo controlled by the throttle stick. About the only disadvantage of a collective pitch system is its cost, which is considerably higher than that of a fixed pitch system, especially after adding the cost of the better radio system required. However, most modelers believe the benefits far outweigh the added cost. Again, the end of this chapter provides a more detailed discussion.

ARF vs. TRADITIONAL KIT

One of the easiest decisions to make will be whether you want to purchase a kit that must be assembled or an Almost-Ready-to-Fly model. The deciding factors here are mostly personal, such as how much time and mechanical experience you have and whether an experienced heli pilot is available to help you with construction questions. Although there is a much greater selection of kits than of ARFs, the improved quality and performance of the latest generation of ARF helicopter models make them worth considering. In fact, if your mechanical or modeling experience is limited, choosing an ARF is a good way to be sure of starting out with an airworthy craft.

CONSTRUCTION MATERIALS

The most common materials used on modern helicopter kits include aluminum, steel, and several types of plastic. Steel is used for the several shafts incorporated in each helicopter kit. The most common types of plastic used are nylon and glass-filled nylon for major components. Bushings are made of a material similar to Teflon.

Most of the larger kits use aluminum for the main frames. These are either flat or formed sheets, with many holes punched out for the bolts that hold the assemblies in place. The ARF kits use molded plastic side frames, not aluminum. Then parts such as bearing holder blocks are usually already molded into the plastic frame, and you don't need to add them later in construction, like you would with a kit. This helps to keep the parts count down and simplifies construction.

The main rotor head can be constructed of either aluminum or plastic. The trend lately has been toward plastic, which helps lower manufacturing costs, and there is no noticeable difference in strength or performance—except in extremely cold weather. Some types of plastic become brittle as the temperature drops. Under these conditions, a hard landing can cause damage that would not be expected under normal conditions.

The landing gear, or *struts*, can also be made of aluminum or plastic. Plastic (such as nylon) is very popular here because it absorbs the shock of hard landings much better than metal does. The skids themselves are always made of aluminum tubing. If the kit you choose comes with all-metal landing gear, a plastic version can be purchased later as a replacement (FIG. 3-2).

POD AND BOOM

In this country, the *pod and boom* is by far the most popular helicopter fuselage style. This type has a molded plastic canopy on the front to cover the radio installation and give the helicopter some shape, and uses a metal tube for the tailboom. The tail rotor gearbox is mounted to the end of the tube. To drive the tail rotor, a metal wire or rubber belt is usually hidden inside the tailboom. This makes for a very strong but lightweight helicopter that is easy to assemble and maintain.

SCALE HELICOPTERS

The other type of fuselage to consider is the *fully enclosed fuselage*, which usually means a scale helicopter. Scale helis are much more popular in Europe than in the United States, but they seem to be gaining in popularity here.

A scale helicopter is certainly more attractive to look at and is easier to see in flight due to the larger side area. But there are some disadvantages, and complexity would have to be near the top of the list.

The word "building" becomes a more appropriate term when assembling a scale helicopter because so much skill is necessary. There is more work to be done with wood, fiberglass, and surface preparation before painting, and, once completed, maintenance and adjustments are not as simple because of the limited access to the mechanical parts of the

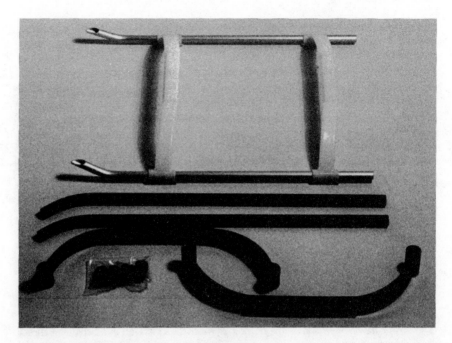

3-2 The Tuff Struts by Miniature Aircraft USA consist of nylon struts and aluminum skids. They are available in two sizes and two colors and will fit most helicopters on the market. Tuff Struts are included with X-Cell helicopter kits.

helicopter. Some fuselages are better than others in respect to access to the mechanics.

For the ultimate in realism, fuselages are available that have been patterned after full-size helicopters. Most larger fuselages are molded in fiberglass, while some of the smaller models are molded in plastic (FIG. 3-3). In addition, with most scale helicopters, the aluminum tailboom

3-3 This Long Ranger III, from Schluter, is a fine example of a fuselage patterned after a full-size helicopter.

found on pod-and-boom helicopters is not used. Instead, the fiberglass fuselage and plywood formers hold the tail rotor assembly in place (FIG. 3-4).

3-4 This cutaway view shows the helicopter mechanics installed in a Schluter Ecureuil fiberglass fuselage.

A fairly new type of helicopter fuselage to consider is the nonscale, fully enclosed type. Several of these are available on the market, and the number of choices is sure to grow. A fully enclosed fuselage offers some of the simplicity of the pod-and-boom helicopter and the nice appearance of a scale helicopter, without making the owner feel obligated to put a lot of effort into an accurate scale paint job.

Is it worth building a scale helicopter? I think it is, but with a few reservations. First, it is much better to learn to fly with a pod-and-boom helicopter: It just isn't worth all the effort to build a scale helicopter before you are an accomplished pilot. Secondly, I would suggest that once you learn to fly well, it is still worth having a pod-and-boom helicopter to fly *in addition to* any scale helicopter that you might be interested in building. It's much harder to relax when flying a scale helicopter when you know the amount of effort that went into it.

ENGINES

Most helicopters available today use variations of the standard two-cycle glow engine that is so popular in RC aircraft. In many cases, the same engine that is used in fixed-wing aircraft is also quite suitable for helicopter flying. A few helicopter kits on the market offer a small, gasoline-powered engine, but these models are generally on the upper extreme of the size range, and they're not as popular. Since the gasoline-powered models usually include the engine with the kit, there is little to say about them, so I'll focus on the glow fuel powered engines.

What size engine to buy should be a fairly simple choice because the size range is dictated by the helicopter that you want to use it in. Normally, a fairly narrow size range is specified, such as .25 to .32, .40 to .50, or .60 cubic inch. Most modelers habitually choose the largest possible engine within the size range specified for a model, whether it is a fixed-wing or helicopter model. This is certainly not a bad idea with a helicopter—not because the extra power is needed to get the model off the ground, but because the reserve power makes it much easier to adjust the engine for satisfactory performance without having to adjust the needle valve for the absolute peak power.

Some modelers have a hard time resisting the urge to over-power their latest project, a practice that carries over somewhat to helicopter modeling, but not as easily as with fixed-wing aircraft. The motor mount is usually an integral part of the helicopter frame and can only accommodate a limited range of engine case dimensions. In most cases, the .50-size helicopter is the only type that can easily mount a larger engine because many .50-size helicopters are based very closely on the .60-size versions of the same model, with many parts being interchangeable. However, if you want to use a .60 engine, I suggest you start out with the right size kit. The rotor blade and corresponding tailboom lengths are chosen by the kit manufacturers, so they will match the power that is available from the recommended engines.

Most of the major engine manufacturers have special engines in their product line specifically designed for helicopter use. These engines are based very closely on engines of the same size that are used in aircraft. They do, however, have one or more special features that make them more desirable for helicopter use.

The most common feature that is included in a helicopter engine is a *heat sink head*, which is a cylinder head that is larger than normal with extra cooling fins to help maintain a normal operating temperature in the demanding environment of a model helicopter (FIG. 3-5). Keeping the engine cool is sure to improve the reliability and durability of the engine. This becomes even more important when using the engine in a fully enclosed fuselage, where there is less cooling air available.

The next common feature on a helicopter engine is a special carburetor. It might include an extra mixture control, called a mid-range adjustment, which is used to fine-tune the fuel mixture at approximately half throttle, where most helicopter flying is done. Some of the most popular carburetors used as replacements on other brands of engines are the Webra Pro-mix and the Supertigre Carburetor. Both of these do extremely well without the mid-range adjustment because the manufacturer did an excellent job of designing the proper mixture setting into the carb. If the engine you buy has a separate mid-range setting, you'll probably find that you use it very little, with everyday adjustments being handled by the high-end needle valve. Nonetheless, it's nice having the potential to adjust low, mid-range, and high mixtures separately.

Some brands of helicopter engines have a different size crankshaft extension compared to the aircraft version, particularly in the .60 size.

3-5 This Webra Speed .28 is typical of most helicopter engines. A large heat-sink head is used to aid cooling. A high-quality carburetor is furnished to provide consistent performance.

Before installing an engine in your helicopter, it is necessary to mount the fan and clutch to the engine. Most helicopter kits come with a clutch that is drilled to fit a 1/4-inch crankshaft. Most .60-size aircraft engines have a 5/16-inch shaft size, or occasionally 8 mm. Therefore, it is quite common for the engine manufacturer, when designing a helicopter version of an engine, to switch to a smaller shaft size to eliminate the need for drilling out the fan that is included with the helicopter kit. This is more beneficial with some kits than others, so be sure to read through the kit instructions before purchasing an engine based on this feature alone.

Most engines are available either with a ringed piston or with an ABC piston-and-sleeve assembly. ABC refers to an aluminum piston riding in a chrome-plated brass sleeve, although there are variations such as nickel plating, aluminum sleeves with chrome plating, etc. The ringed versions are slightly less expensive and have the benefit of being easier to turn over with an electric starter. The ABC type has a reputation of being more powerful and more durable, and it is also more tolerant of a lean needle-valve setting.

In a very dusty environment, the ringed engine might actually prove to be more economical to operate because the ring alone can be replaced without having to replace the entire piston and sleeve. If abrasive dirt is anticipated, it might be best to fit an air filter to the engine as a precaution.

The last variation available is a ringed piston riding in a chrome plated sleeve. While this would seem to be the best of both worlds, it has not become popular yet.

START SYSTEMS

While several types of starting systems are used in model helicopters, the simplest type is the belt-start system (FIG. 3-6). With this type, the fan hub that is mounted to the engine crankshaft has a groove around it that is used to engage a pulley connected to an electric starter. After the motor is running, the belt is tucked out of the way until needed again. The belt-start system is popular on the .30-size helicopters and also on the Kalt line of helicopter kits. Because there are less alignment problems due to the lack of a start shaft extension, the mounting of the fan and clutch assembly becomes less crucial. On the other hand, it is inconvenient to fasten the belt out of the way when not in use, and it is often awkward holding an electric starter on the side of a helicopter while trying to keep the belt lined up properly.

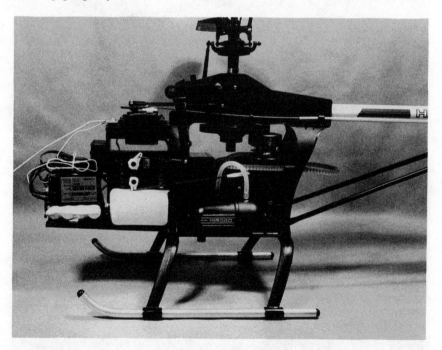

3-6 The Hirobo Shuttle ZX features a belt-start engine. The starting pulley is located directly below the clutch bell, and the starting belt is tucked out of the way when not in use.

The other popular starting system is the cone-start type, which usually involves an extension shaft mounted onto the part of the clutch that is constantly driven by the motor. The shaft runs through one or two bearing blocks to the top of the helicopter frame. A tapered cone or other type of adaptor is mounted there. (This matches up to a rubber adaptor on the electric starter extension.)

The cone can be mounted directly on the end of the engine crankshaft, in helicopter engines where such a cone would be accessible. This

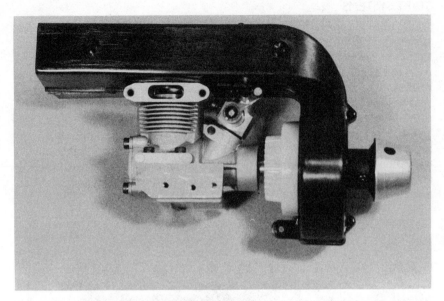

3-7 The engine, clutch, and fan assembly from a Kalt Enforcer clearly show the start cone located on the end of the fan. A dial indicator is not necessary with this type of design.

3-8 A large opening in the canopy provides access to the starting cone on this Kalt Enforcer. You can use a standard aircraft starter without a special adaptor.

type of installation has all the benefits of a cone-start system, without the disadvantages of using a start shaft (FIGS. 3-7 and 3-8).

The cone-start system can be simultaneously more convenient and more complicated than the belt-start system. Chapter 4 explains what is involved in properly installing a start shaft extension before mounting the motor in the helicopter.

HELI RADIOS

The type of radio you decide to buy will be influenced by many things, such as the price range, whether or not you are just "trying out" helicopters, and what type of helicopter you have chosen (FIGS. 3-9 and 3-10). To start with the basics, a fixed pitch helicopter, such as an MFA Sport 500 by Hobby Lobby, or the GMP Rebel, does not require a special radio. You can use the same radio you might already be using to fly a model airplane. On this type of helicopter, there is no need for the electronic mixing circuits included in even the most basic helicopter radios. As I mentioned earlier, the main disadvantage is the slower control response, but this is the price you pay for simplicity—and it might be the right choice for you as an inexpensive introduction to helicopter flight.

The next step up from the basic four-channel radio would be a five- or six-channel helicopter radio. Definitely included in this type of heli radio will be at least two mixing circuits.

3-9 The Futaba FP-T5NLH is an example of a basic helicopter radio transmitter with the most essential features, such as pitch mixing and revolution compensation.

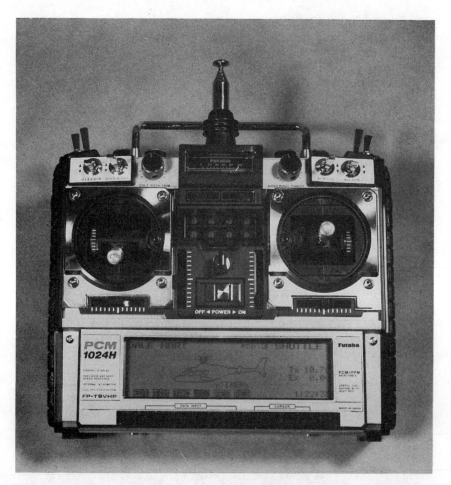

3-10 On the other end of the spectrum, the Futaba FP-T9VHP transmitter has virtually every feature conceivable. The computer control system remembers the adjustments for up to six separate models.

The first mixing circuit is the collective pitch mixing, which is used to control the throttle and pitch servos independently but simultaneously with the throttle control stick. When properly adjusted, as the throttle stick is advanced, the rpm of the helicopter rotor system increases until it reaches the proper speed. From then on, as the throttle stick is pushed farther forward, the collective pitch servo increases the pitch, and therefore the load on the engine. Meanwhile the throttle servo opens the carburetor barrel farther to increase power and maintain it, without increasing the rpm. As this happens, the thrust from the rotor will increase to the point where the helicopter lifts off, and then continues to climb.

All of this interaction between the throttle and pitch servos can be accomplished with one servo controlling both pushrods, but it is very difficult. By using the mixing circuit, it becomes possible to adjust the trim of each function independently of the other. Without this feature, adjusting the idle speed of the engine would have an adverse effect on the setting of the collective pitch. Many of the advanced features included in better helicopter radios center around this pitch-mixing circuit.

The next feature sure to be included in even the most basic heli radio is the tail rotor compensation mixing circuit. As the collective pitch setting changes on a helicopter, the amount of pitch needed at the tail rotor to stop the helicopter from rotating also changes. The tail rotor mixing circuit makes it possible for the radio to make these corrections for you by coupling the tail rotor, or *rudder servo*, to the throttle stick position. The type of adjustments will vary with the radio, but all serve the same purpose.

Now, it's time to move on to the throttle control itself. No mixing circuits are involved here, but quite a few features are available to make the throttle respond in the desired fashion.

Every self-respecting heli radio is sure to have a switch that is labeled throttle hold. The throttle-hold switch is used to disconnect the throttle and pitch servos by moving the throttle servo to a predetermined spot, usually idle, while allowing the pilot to have full control of the pitch servo—a procedure used to perform autorotation. The ability to set the throttle to idle makes it possible to practice this maneuver without having to restart the motor after each landing. This is one of the few basic helicopter radio features that cannot be duplicated mechanically, but it is also one of the least essential for beginners.

The next most common feature will most likely be hi-idle, or idle-up, which, as its name implies, is used to give a higher idle. While you won't use hi idle much while learning to hover, you'll appreciate it more once you achieve forward flight. What hi idle does is increase the throttle opening to approximately quarter-throttle when the throttle stick is all the way down at idle. As the stick is pushed forward, the throttle continues to open as usual. As half stick is reached, the throttle position will be the same, with or without hi idle turned on, and this remains true as the throttle is increased all the way to full stick.

As you fly your helicopter around, preparing to land, there will be times when you need to reduce the collective pitch to allow the helicopter to descend. Without hi idle turned on, the rotor speed would decrease as the throttle stick is pulled back to reduce pitch, causing the controls to become sluggish and making it hard to stop the descent. Using hi idle keeps the rotor speed constant throughout the entire throttle stick range. An adjustment knob on the transmitter allows the pilot to fine-tune the amount of throttle that is added at low stick.

Another feature related to the throttle is an adjustment for setting the amount of servo travel at high- and possibly low-stick positions. Whether it is labeled as such or not, this is merely the familiar end-point adjustment, used when first setting up a helicopter in the workshop to make sure there are no binds in the linkages while still maintaining full control movement. The same thing can be accomplished, but not quite as easily, by changing the position and length of the servo arm. Having a separate adjustment for high and low throttle makes it easier to set the middle position properly, knowing that the high and low adjustments can be used afterwards to stop the pushrod from binding or not moving far enough.

Next on the list, but not always found on less expensive radios, is a feature called hovering throttle. It is a knob that allows you to increase or decrease the amount of throttle opening while the helicopter is in a hover. The hovering throttle knob is similar to the normal throttle trim lever, but the former works at half stick rather than at idle, and has no effect at low stick or full stick. This is great for adjusting the rotor speed or the stick position where the helicopter will lift off the ground. The same thing can be accomplished, to some extent, using hovering pitch, but there are times when one is better than the other.

If hovering throttle is not included on your radio, you can achieve the same effect by moving the throttle servo arm. However, this method is more complicated and it is much harder to experiment without having the adjustment on the transmitter.

The last feature to mention is idle up 2, a feature found only on the more sophisticated radios. It is used for aerobatics which involve brief periods of inverted flight, such as a roll or an Immelmann. When idle up 2 is engaged, the throttle never goes below a certain position, usually set somewhere around 60 percent throttle opening. This gives a slightly higher rotor speed for aerobatics and allows the use of negative pitch, which is at the lowest throttle stick position, without losing rotor speed because of the throttle closing. While idle up 2 is certainly not an essential feature, it is great for aerobatics. Other features are available on the most sophisticated computer radios, but they are best left to experienced pilots.

Depending on which radio you have chosen, you might also have to decide between AM, FM, and PCM versions. Because of its sensitivity to mechanical noise, AM is not very popular in helicopter circles, so you're left with the choice between FM and PCM. FM works quite well, but PCM goes further to increase reliability by starting with a basic FM system and adding an encoder to the transmitter and a decoder to the receiver to ensure the integrity of the transmitted control information. The choice here will usually be decided by how much you are willing to pay. The PCM systems generally cost about $100 more than an equivalent FM system.

TOOLS

The tools you will need to get started will vary with the difficulty of the kit you have chosen. To complete an ARF, only the bare essentials will be required. If you have been involved in other forms of modeling, you will probably have these tools on hand.

You will need a set of straight and phillips screwdrivers covering the small to mid-size range. A set of small metric wrenches are also quite useful. In a pinch, you can make do with a small adjustable wrench.

Assembly will go faster if you have a set of nut drivers. The most important size is 5.5 mm, followed by 7 mm. Most kits include a set of allen wrenches, but allen drivers—allen wrenches mounted in a screw-driver handle—are nicer to use. The most common allen wrench sizes are 1.5 mm, 2 mm, 2.5 mm, 3 mm, and 4 mm. Practically all the bolts used in assembly will need a 2.5-mm allen wrench, and the set screws will need a 1.5-mm allen wrench (FIGS. 3-11 and 3-12).

If the helicopter kit you have chosen uses a starting shaft that is part of the clutch, you'll need a dial indicator to properly align the clutch and start shaft on the motor. Considering the high price of this tool, you might want to try borrowing one the first time.

Once your helicopter is assembled, a pitch gauge will help you adjust the angle of the blades properly. Some kits provide a wood or paper gauge to start with, but the proper tool works much better (FIGS. 3-13 and 3-14). Of course, you can always purchase a pitch gauge at a later date.

Several companies offer a complete set of tools in a carrying case. These sets include all the basic tools and some of the extras that make the job of assembling your helicopter kit and adjusting it easier. If you do not have the basic tools on hand already, it might be worth buying a complete set. The quality is generally quite high, and the selection is appropriate for the intended purpose.

STARTING EQUIPMENT

Once your helicopter is ready to fly, you will need a few basics to get the engine started. Obviously, you will need fuel. All helicopter modelers usually use some type of model aircraft fuel. Some companies make a special

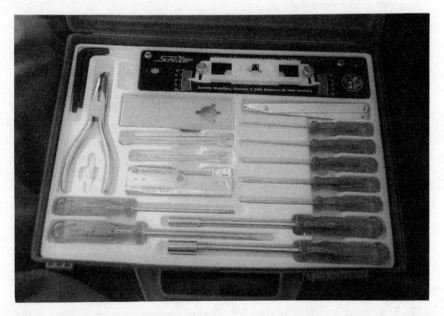

3-11 This Schluter helicopter tool kit is available from Robbe Model Sport. Purchasing a tool kit is an excellent way to get the most important tools for your new hobby.

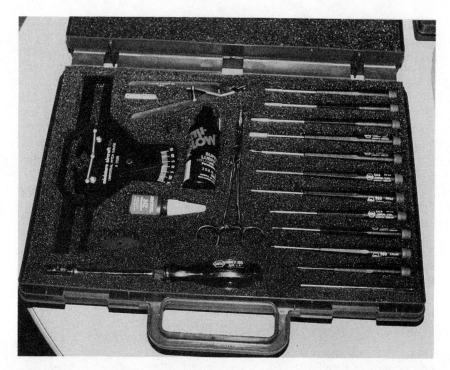

3-12 Several manufacturers offer complete tool kits for helicopter enthusiasts. This tool kit, from Miniature Aircraft USA, includes some specialized tools such as a pitch meter and ball link pliers.

3-13 This pitch gauge from Miniature Aircraft can be used to measure the angle of the rotor blades during adjustments. The flybar must be level and the flat portion of the pitch gauge held parallel with the flybar to obtain an accurate reading.

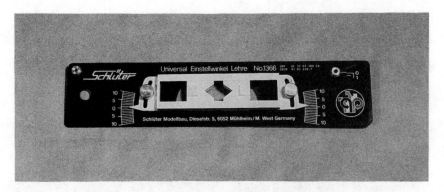

3-14 The pitch gauge by Schluter is a standard one.

blend of model fuel for helicopters that uses all-synthetic oil in the fuel for cleaner burning. The color of this fuel is usually darker than regular model aircraft fuel, making it easier to check the fuel level while the helicopter is in flight.

To get the fuel into the tank, you can use a small hand crank or an electric fuel pump. The hand crank offers simplicity because it does not require a power supply. On the other hand, the electric pump is faster and more convenient.

The glow plug on the engine needs a power supply, and this can be as simple as a 1.5-volt dry-cell battery, or as sophisticated as a power panel with an adjustable output lead for the glow plug. In between, a very popular way to light the glow plug is with a rechargeable 1.5-volt NiCad battery mounted to a glow plug connector. Several brands are available, and most come complete with a charger. The best ones also have a small meter built in to check the condition of the glow plug.

You'll need an electric starter to start the engine, unless the helicopter or engine you have chosen is available with a pull starter (FIG. 3-15). The electric starter is powered by a 12-volt battery. A car battery provides the most power in cold weather, but a motorcycle battery is more convenient for normal conditions.

Many brands and models of electric starters are available on the market. Besides minor differences in quality, the major factor to consider is the power, or torque, of the motor used on the starter. With most helicopter engines, any starter will do. However, if you have chosen an ABC design, it might be wise to get a high-torque starter to make it easier to start the engine when it hasn't been running for some time. ABC engines are harder to turn over because the piston and liner are a much tighter fit than a ringed piston and liner would be.

In addition to the starter, you might also need an extension to connect the starter to the helicopter engine. Many helicopters use a cone on top of the engine start shaft for engaging the starter. The starter uses an extension that has a rubber insert in the end of it, and this extension is available either from the helicopter kit manufacturer or, in some cases, from the starter manufacturer.

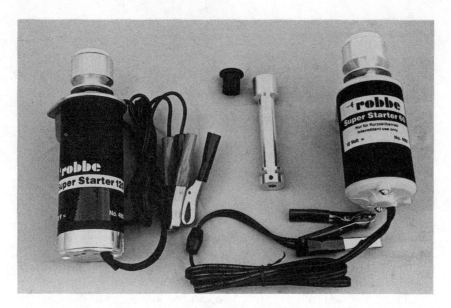

3-15 You'll need an electric starter to start your helicopter's engine. Depending on the mechanical arrangement of your helicopter, you might also need a starter extension.

The major difference between brands is in how well the extension mounts to the starter motor shaft. The best extensions will use four setscrews, spaced 90 degrees apart, to both secure and align themselves with the starter motor shaft. When adjusted properly, the extension should not wobble when the starter is running.

If the helicopter you have chosen uses a belt start, you won't need an extension. Most kits of this type include a rubber v-belt for starting. If not, they are available at most hobby shops. (V-belts are also used for starting RC boats.) Electric starters generally have a groove in the start adaptor that is included for use on model aircraft. If you will be using a belt to start your helicopter engine, be sure the starter you buy also has the needed groove in its start cone.

To keep everything together, you might want to buy one of the special "flight boxes" that are available. You can purchase them either molded in plastic or as a wood kit that has to be assembled and painted or fuel-proofed. A flight box will hold your fuel container, 12-volt battery, starter, a power panel, and an electric fuel pump (FIG. 3-16). Many of them also have one or more drawers for keeping your tools organized. Some even have room to hold a transmitter. If you don't want to buy a flight box right away, a strong cardboard box or plastic crate will do nicely.

3-16 You might want to build or purchase a flight box to hold all the essentials for starting your helicopter. My flight box holds a 12-volt battery, my starter, fuel supply, electric fuel pump, and a power panel.

Chapter 4

Kit assembly

*I*f you have purchased a helicopter kit, you will certainly be anxious to start assembling it. This chapter explains what is involved in assembling the various types of kits available.

INSTRUCTIONS

Before starting to put your new helicopter kit together, first read the instructions to familiarize yourself with the various components and steps. Now re-read the assembly instructions, but this time locate the parts for each step and put them aside. When you are through, you'll know if any parts are missing, and you'll be more familiar with each of the steps and their components.

If your kit has building plans, it is important that you place them someplace where they can be referenced often without being in the way of your work. The easiest way to accomplish this is to hang them up on the wall in front of the work area.

Read and follow the instructions carefully. If something doesn't seem right, re-read the instructions again and review the plans. If you become aggravated, stop and take a break: It's easy to become engrossed during the construction stages and work longer than you are able to concentrate. A carefully built model should set up easily and provide many hours of enjoyable flying, so take your time.

Once you are familiar with the assembly steps, you can prepare to start the construction. The parts in the kit will be packaged in several plastic bags. Some manufacturers divide the parts to match the sequence of assembly in the instructions, making it easy to locate the proper fasteners since they are in the bag with all the other parts needed for that particular step in the process. You might want to have a small tray on hand in which to empty the bag as you start each new step. To avoid confusion, do not open any of the parts bags until you get to that part in the instructions.

Other manufacturers choose to divide the parts by type and subassembly. With this kind of kit, one bag contains all fasteners, another houses all plastic parts for the tail rotor, and still another holds all metal parts for the tail rotor. If the parts of your kit are divided this way, you might want to have several trays or boxes in which to keep the extra parts in each bag until they are needed. Be careful not to lose track of which package each part came from, because the instructions will tell you where to look for them based on the number that was on the parts bag. The easiest way to keep things straight is to put the bag label in the tray holding the parts.

With either type of kit, you have to choose the proper fasteners—whether screw, bolt, washer, or nut—to match what the instructions specify. With some kits, the instructions include a full-size drawing for each size, located either on a separate sheet of paper, or included with each step of the instructions, with only the required parts shown. Instructions for other kits give a measurement for the fastener, and you then have to find the proper parts using a ruler.

The measurements given are metric. A typical size would be a 3-×-25 cap screw (FIG. 4-1). Such a screw would have a socket head to accept an allen wrench; its diameter would be 3 mm, and its length from under the head to the tip would be 25 mm. When the instructions call for a 3 mm bolt, they are referring to the size of the thread, not the allen wrench that is used with it. The 3 mm size, the most common, uses a 2.5 mm allen wrench.

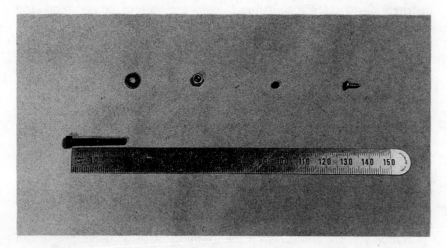

4-1 Socket head cap screws are measured from the bottom of the head to the end of the bolt. The 3 mm bolt shown here measures 25 mm long.

The smaller 2 mm bolt is commonly used to mount the center of the ball links to the swashplate, bellcranks, and servos. This size uses a 1.5 mm allen wrench. The most common size of set screw has a 3 mm diameter, but since it has no head on the end, a 1.5 mm wrench is used to fit the socket that is stamped inside one end.

If you are assembling a helicopter with plastic side frames, you'll find yourself using a lot of *self-tapping screws*, or sheet metal screws, which typically have phillips heads. If you have a cordless electric screwdriver on hand, you might want to use it to join the two halves of the frames, since so many screws are necessary here. Be careful not to overtighten the screws when working with plastic parts, or you might accidentally strip out the holes.

During stages of assembly, the instructions might call for you to use a liquid thread locker. Use only what comes with the kit, because some types will attack certain kinds of plastics. If your kit does not supply a liquid thread locker, shop for any brand that will not attack plastics. Remember that at some point you might have to remove the nuts and bolts you are now locking together, so you don't want to use stud-and-bearing-mount-strength thread locker on the blade holders, engine mounts, etc. When you use thread locker, do so sparingly, and don't get it on anything you don't wish to be locked together. A little bit goes a long way.

Most kits use nylock or lock nuts for greater reliability. These nuts have a ring of plastic or nylon on the outer edge, and the nut is slightly smaller in outside diameter where the nylon is. Before you can finger-tighten locking nuts, you will have to use tools. Tighten them the same as regular nuts, making sure the screw protrudes slightly and that the nylon is facing out. Also, the threads must be flush with the outside of the nut to ensure proper locking qualities.

SET SCREWS

All kits call for *set screws* or grub screws during assembly, usually for drive-train connections for the tail rotor and for control-arm connections in the rotor head. I recommend that you use thread locker in these cases because vibration can loosen the screws at the wrong moment. For the 1.5 mm size, a hardened driver is best. If you do not have one, use the short arm of the allen wrench on the head to tighten the screw.

BEARINGS

The three general types of ball bearings used on an RC helicopter are the open bearing, the shielded bearing, and the sealed bearing. On the most basic kind, an *open bearing*, the balls are visible from either side.

On a *shielded bearing*, a metal disk covers the balls to keep dirt out. The disk is a snap-fit into the outer race and a loose fit to the inner race. If the manufacturer intends grease to be able to get into a bearing from one side while keeping dirt out from the other, a single shield will be used. Such an arrangement is often found when a pair of bearings are mounted in a bearing block or gear case that is filled with grease. The bearings on each end have a single shield facing the outside of the case, and any bearings not exposed are unshielded ones. The grease can then circulate through all bearings from the inside, but the shields help to keep the grease inside the case and the dirt outside.

A sealed bearing is similar to a shielded bearing in construction, but a sealed bearing uses a tight-fitting rubber seal instead of a metal shield. Sealed bearings are packed with grease at the factory but cannot be relubricated without removing the seal—unfortunately, a procedure that usually damages the seal. In addition, the seal, with its tight fit, causes more drag than other types of bearings. For this reason, along with the higher cost, sealed bearings are not common on model helicopters.

Besides the radial ball bearing, which is the most common, thrust bearings and shoulder bearings are also used in model helicopters. *Thrust bearings* are usually found in the blade holders, both main and tail rotor. They are used to allow smooth rotation for pitch change while under load from centrifugal force. Generally, thrust bearings are only required on large models using weighted main rotor blades. Some designs allow the addition of thrust bearings, and the best kits include them from the start. The optimum design for blade holders uses a thrust bearing and two radial bearings to support the blade.

Shoulder bearings are used in small sizes to take the place of nylon bushings. A small *flange*, or shoulder, on one edge prevents the bearing from slipping through the hole it is mounted in. Shoulder bearings are often found in the control system of the helicopter—usually in the mixing arms and bellcranks because these parts benefit from the smooth, effortless movement provided by the ball bearings. However, many kits use molded nylon bushings in these locations to help keep costs down, and these work better than you might expect, since the parts in the control system are not rotating at high speed as the shafts on the helicopter are. Also, a properly fitted bushing can actually have less play in it than a bearing.

The main shaft, tail rotor drive shaft, and the engine start shaft (if so equipped) are supported by ball bearings. These bearings must be held in the proper locations on the helicopter by a bearing block. The construction of the bearing blocks varies with different kits. Generally, though, if the helicopter has metal side frames, the bearing blocks are composed of either aluminum or plastic. If the blocks are made of aluminum, the ball bearings are simply pressed in place (usually at the factory).

On many of the newer kits, the blocks will be made of plastic. They are molded in two pieces, with a left and right half. A bearing is placed in one half, and the second side is placed over it and pressed in place. The bearing should be a tight fit in the block, but nonetheless, apply a small amount of epoxy glue to each plastic shell where the bearing will go. The glue will stop the outer race of the bearing from spinning or wobbling inside the block. It is important not to get any glue on the part of the bearing that rotates. After the bearing blocks are assembled, they will be held together by the bolts passing through the side frames.

On a helicopter kit using molded plastic side frames, the bearing blocks are usually molded directly into the side frames (FIG. 4-2). A small dab of glue is still a good idea to make sure the fit is not too loose.

If the bearing is a loose fit in its holder, the shaft will wobble slightly and will get worse with time as the outer race of the bearing spins and

4-2 Plastic side frames, like these from a Kyosho Concept 30, have the bearing holders molded as an integral part of the frame. In this photo the control bellcranks have already been installed.

continues to wear away the inside of the holder. You shouldn't have this problem with metal holders, but—just in case—a small amount of epoxy should fill the gap. You could also use a center punch on edge of the block to pinch the bearing in place.

If the bearings are a loose fit on the shaft they support, the shaft might rotate inside the bearing, rather than the bearing itself rotating, causing the shaft to wear and further aggravating the problem. To prevent this from happening, put a small amount of thread-locking compound, such as Loctite, on the shaft where it will contact the bearing (FIG. 4-3). Be very careful not to get any Loctite anywhere on the bearing except on the bore. If the shaft is already a loose fit, you might want to use a special grade of Loctite called "stud and bearing mount" that is thicker than normal.

During assembly, any bearings that are open on at least one side should be packed with grease. Put some grease between the inner and outer races, and rub it into the balls. Bearing blocks are usually assembled with the bearing shields on the side, facing outwards. The sides facing the center of the block are open to allow grease to circulate. The area in the block between the bearings should be filled with grease during assembly; the same holds true for the tail rotor gearbox. The instructions for your kit should explain exactly what areas to grease.

Wherever one metal part rotates on another metal part, apply a light coating of oil during assembly. Where plastic parts are involved, use an oil specially designed to be compatible with plastic. Oils containing a solvent, such as WD-40, should be avoided in these areas.

4-3 Notice the wear that is evident from the shaft slipping inside the bearings on this plastic bearing block and tail-rotor drive-gear shaft. You can prevent this by using thread-locking compound on the shaft during assembly.

ENGINE INSTALLATION

To obtain the best performance from your helicopter, proper engine installation is crucial. Before you can install the engine, however, you have to mount one or more parts to the end of the crankshaft.

Practically all helicopters will have a cooling fan attached to the engine. A plastic duct carries the air to the cylinder head where it is needed to cool the engine.

Next, something is needed to transfer the engine's power to the helicopter drive train, usually a centrifugal clutch. However, some designs use a drive belt pulley instead, and, in such a case, the clutch might be located elsewhere in the system.

A clutch bell fits around the clutch. When the engine reaches the proper speed, the clutch engages, causing the clutch bell to turn with it. A gear mounted to the clutch bell then drives the rotor blades of the helicopter through the remainder of the drive train.

Finally, you need a way to start the engine. The two most common methods are belt-start and cone-start systems, and these must be installed before the engine is. With belt start, all that is needed on the helicopter is a pulley that is directly connected to the engine. The cone start system can be either quite simple or complicated, depending on the location of the engine. Traditionally, the engine is mounted vertically at the bottom of the helicopter frames, with the crankshaft pointing up. Such an installation uses a drive shaft, again connected to the engine, that extends out the top of the helicopter mechanics. One or two bearing blocks are used to support it. Finally, a cone is fastened to the top, which mates with a rubber adaptor on the electric starter.

To simplify matters, the latest trend in cone-start systems is to relocate the engine position so that the cone is mounted directly to the end of the crankshaft but is still accessible for starting. Usually, this means pointing the engine toward the rear of the helicopter. The drive train is a bit more complicated with this method, but the lack of a start shaft simplifies engine installation substantially.

A third system that is starting to gain popularity is the pull start, which is similar to what is found on a lawn mower. The pull start is offered by some engine manufacturers on the backplate of the engine as an option. Alternatively, some helicopter kits have a pull start available to take the place of a starting pulley. Before buying an engine-mounted pull start, make sure it will fit on your helicopter—there has to be enough room behind the engine for the starter. Generally engine-mounted pull starts are only used on helicopters that were originally designed for belt start rather than cone start.

The direct-mount cone start is similar in design and simplicity to the belt start system, but it is easier to use when starting the engine. The kit instructions will explain the proper order to mount the fan, clutch, and starting components on the engine.

To adequately tighten the nut on the end of the crankshaft, you need to find a way to stop the engine shaft from rotating. The best alternative is to put a piece of thin plywood into the exhaust port, between the top of the piston and the cylinder wall (FIG. 4-4). If you choose, you can remove

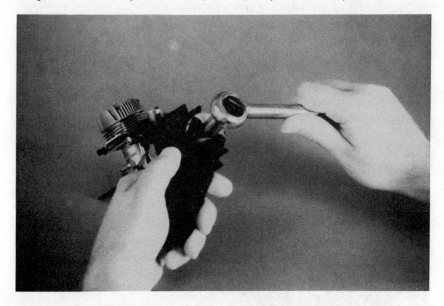

4-4 Use a socket wrench to securely tighten the nut on the engine crankshaft. You might be able to find a special tool that will stop the fan hub from turning during this procedure, such as the GMP tool shown here.

the carburetor and place a wooden dowel into the opening in the crankshaft. **Note:** Under no circumstances should anything harder than wood be inserted into the engine! Even brass or aluminum could cause permanent damage. Do, however, make every effort to get the drive nut as tight as possible: It is very frustrating to have it come loose when you try to start the engine.

Ideally, heli engines should have left-handed threads on the crankshafts instead of the right-handed threads they now use. As they are currently designed, the force used to start the engine also tries to loosen the drive nut, unless it is tight enough.

The traditional cone-start system is a bit more complicated. Not only does it have more parts, but is also requires you to align the starting shaft. Typically, the fan is mounted first. Your kit should provide a tool to hold the fan hub while tightening the drive nut, which should also stop the crankshaft from turning. If not, use a piece of wood (as explained earlier). If the fan is a self-centering design with tapered collets, go ahead and tighten it. If not, just gently tighten the nut.

You must center the clutch and start shaft on the crankshaft first because later it will be mounted to the fan hub. I recommend using a dial indicator to test for proper alignment. Place the small finger on the dial indicator against the outer edge of the fan hub, and slowly turn the crankshaft. As the hub rotates off-center, the needle on the dial indicator will move, indicating the amount of *runout* that is present, which shows the degree of misalignment between the engine shaft and the fan hub.

Most dial indicators are marked in one-thousandths of an inch. Your goal should be to get the two parts within .002 inch, or two-thousandths of an inch (two lines on the gauge, if calibrated in inches). Any more runout than this will cause excessive vibration, possibly leading to premature wear of the helicopter parts, fuel foaming, and possible radio failure (FIG. 4-5).

4-5 A dial indicator is being used to measure the runout, or wobble, in the start shaft of a Schluter Champion. Total runout should be less than .002 inches.

Next, the clutch is mounted to the fan hub. If the start shaft is attached to the clutch, as is common, then the clutch must be perfectly centered on the fan hub. To test this, use the dial indicator to check the runout in the start shaft directly above the clutch. The mounting holes are slightly oversized to allow for adjustment. When the clutch is perfectly centered, remove one screw at a time, apply some thread-locking compound, and tighten the screw.

Finally, the runout at the top of the start shaft should be checked (FIG. 4-6). Adjustments are made here by gently bending the shaft at the bottom, where it is attached to the clutch. Be careful not to bend it in the

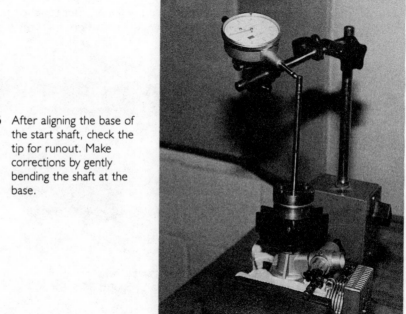

4-6 After aligning the base of the start shaft, check the tip for runout. Make corrections by gently bending the shaft at the base.

middle, or the shaft will no longer be straight. The runout at the top is a bit less crucial because the length of the shaft gives enough flexibility to absorb some misalignment. Five-thousandths of an inch (.005) is acceptable, but it shouldn't be hard to get it better than this.

To use the dial indicator, the engine must be firmly mounted to a vise, a table, or a piece of wood. The dial indicator is held in position by one or more adjustable rods supported by a magnetic base. A vise is the easiest way to mount the indicator; otherwise, some improvising is in order. Use a C clamp to hold the dial indicator base in place if it is mounted to the table or to wood.

As you've probably noticed, a good deal of precision is required to install an engine properly. To help reduce the level of exactness, a few of the latest helicopter designs are retaining the start shaft design, but are separating the start shaft from the engine. When the pilot wants to start the engine, he pushes down on the start cone. The start shaft moves down and a drive pin engages with the fan hub. After the engine is started, a spring pushes the start shaft up away from the engine. With this design, the start shaft cannot cause vibration because it is only turning during the starting procedure, not during flight.

MUFFLERS

A muffler should be used to reduce the noise level of your helicopter. Depending on what kit you have chosen, you might be able to use the muffler supplied by the engine manufacturer. Because of the varying requirements of helicopter designs; however, not all engines are sold with a muffler kit. Most helicopter kit manufacturers sell a muffler for each particular model, so be sure to ask whether it will fit the engine you have chosen (FIGS. 4-7 and 4-8).

4-7 Different helicopters require different manifold and exhaust configurations. These mufflers from Miniature Aircraft USA cover most popular .30-size models.

To improve the consistency and reliability of your engine, run a pressure line from the muffler to the fuel tank. By using muffler pressure, the engine receives a much steadier supply of fuel and, as a result, the needle valve settings do not change noticeably during a flight.

The only other line from the tank should go to the carburetor; this is the line that goes to a *clunk*, or weight, inside the tank. The purpose of the clunk is to ensure that the engine can draw fuel while the helicopter goes through turns, even after the fuel level is low.

GEAR ALIGNMENT

Once all the components are attached to the engine crankshaft and aligned as necessary, it is time to mount the engine in the helicopter. The procedure will vary with the design of the helicopter, so be sure to follow the directions. The main concern is that the drive gear or drive belt is

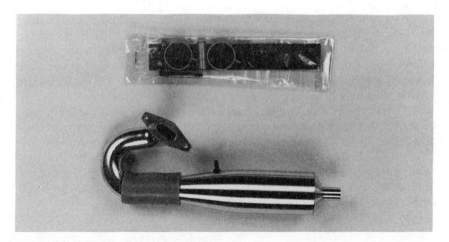

4-8 Tuned exhaust systems are available to fit most helicopter and engine combinations. They provide a slight increase in power, while still quieting the engine.

aligned properly, and gear mesh (if appropriate) is set correctly.

With the typical gear drive, a small gear called the *pinion* is fastened to the top of the clutch bell. This drives the main gear of the helicopter. A slight clearance between the two gears is required for smooth operation. If a piece of paper can be run through the gears without jamming, then the clearance is loose enough (FIG. 4-9). On the other hand, if the gears are too loose, the teeth might fail because the load will be carried by only the outer edges.

4-9 Confirm proper gear mesh by running a piece of paper between the gears. If the gears turn without binding but a slight drag is noticeable, then the gear mesh is correct.

If your helicopter uses a cone start with a starting shaft, then the next step is to put the start-shaft bearing block(s) in. They should drop in place between the side frames, but if not, you might have to shift the engine sideways in its mount to allow the start shaft to stay centered between the frames. Once everything is lined up correctly, you can fully tighten the engine mounting bolts.

The tail rotor drive gear must be meshed properly with the main gear, following the same procedure as with the pinion gear/main gear fit. Usually, the tail rotor drive gear is attached to a short shaft supported by two ball bearings in a block. Move the block around until the gear mesh is correct, being careful to keep the drive gear shaft parallel to the surface of the main gear (or perpendicular to the main shaft). Premature wear can result from poor alignment.

BLADE COVERING

If your kit has wood blades, they will have to be covered with one of the two available types of blade coverings, self-adhesive and heat-shrink. Both are fairly easy to work with, but each have their idiosyncrasies. One or the other type will be supplied in the kit.

Self-adhesive covering

Let's talk about self-adhesive first. With this type it is wise to paint the root end of the blade first. This keeps the blade from absorbing moisture as well as fuel and oil. Painting the root is easier before you cover it because you can use a spray can. Be sure that the paint you are using is fuel-proof, as some fuel will find its way into the rotor blades. Regardless of the type of covering, sanding the blades with a fine- to medium-grit sandpaper results in a very smooth finish.

Wash your hands before you handle the covering. Once you are ready to cover your blades, lay the covering material on the table with the plastic side down, and carefully peel off the backing. Once all of the adhesive is revealed, make a mark 3/8 inch from the closest edge at each end. This is where the covering material will wrap around the trailing edge of the blade.

With the root (blade holder) end facing left, slowly set the blade trailing-edge-down onto the covering. Line up the trailing edge with the marks, and line up the tip end of the blade holder with the left edge of the covering material (FIG. 4-10). Start with the blade facing straight up. Once the trailing edge is making full contact with the covering material and the marks line up correctly, slowly roll the blade forward onto the covering material. When the blade touches the adhesive, you can pick up the blade and turn it over. The covering material is now properly positioned on the blade.

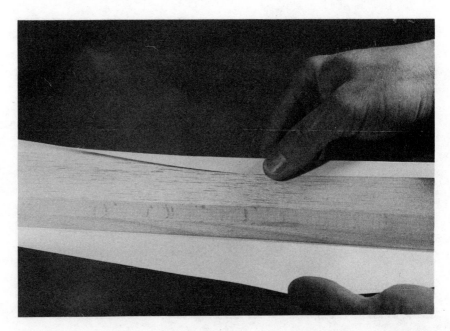

4-10 Self-adhesive blade covering is being wrapped around the trailing edge of a wooden blade. You might find that it helps to work from the center of the blade toward each tip.

Starting at the trailing edge, rub the covering material down firmly. At this point, you are working on the top side of the blade. Hold the covering away from the blade as you approach the leading edge. Once the covering is smoothly rubbed down onto the main part of the blade, the 3/8 inch extension at the trailing edge can be folded over and pressed in place on the bottom side of the blade.

With the trailing edge taken care of on both sides, you can now concentrate on the leading edge. Hold the covering material away from the blade with one hand, while rubbing it down with the other. Carefully work your way around the leading edge of the blade. Once the covering wraps around to the other side, gently smooth it down toward the trailing edge. There should be enough material to overlap the 3/8 inch that was folded over from the top of the blade (FIG. 4-11).

Now you can trim the excess covering away; a sharp knife or scissors works well. If you want, you can seal the edge of the covering to the wood at the root and tip. Thin cyanoacrylate (CyA) glue or paint is suitable.

You should now have a smooth-looking (and feeling) blade! One note: If your rotor direction is counter-clockwise, the bottom of the blade will face up when the root end is on the right, with the leading edge (thicker edge) facing away.

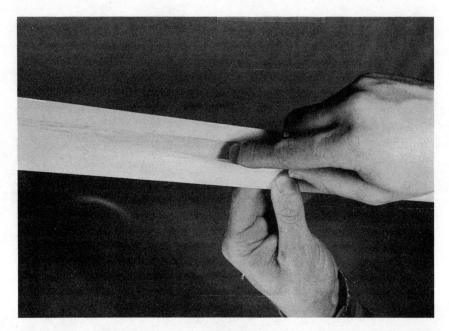

4-11 The self-adhesive blade covering is being wrapped around the leading edge of the blade. The covering will overlap at the trailing edge; this should be on the bottom of the blade for best appearance. Cover both blades identically.

Heat-shrink covering

To use heat-shrink blade covering, you need a source of heat. A hand-held hair dryer is sufficient, but you can use steam from a tea kettle with very good results. Your local hobby shop should carry an item called a *heat gun*, which is intended for covering airplanes with iron-on coverings, but it works well for heat-shrink blade covering as well. If you use a heat gun, take care not to melt the covering material.

Sand the blade to a smooth finish as you would for the self-adhesive covering, only you don't have to paint the root end because the shrink tubing will cover the entire length of the blade. Slide the shrink tubing over the blade (you might have to cut the tubing in half, as it is usually one piece for both blades), and make sure it is centered on the blade. Starting from the middle of the blade, apply the heat source. If you are using a heat gun or a blow dryer, you might find it easier to lay the heat source on the work area and hold the blade in your hands.

Work towards one end, and turn the blade over frequently. Keep tension on the excess tubing, and try not to keep the heat pointed on one spot too long. When you reach the end, pull harder and direct the heat at the end. When you feel the shrinking stop, remove the heat. Most wrinkles and bubbles will work themselves out. Now go back to the center of the blade and work towards the other end.

At the root end, the blade is cut diagonally from the trailing edge toward the leading edge to allow the blade to fold without denting the trailing edge of the blade. When you are doing the root end, try to pull the tubing diagonally towards the leading edge (FIG. 4-12).

When you are finished covering your blades, trim the extra covering off each end with a scissors or knife. You should seal the tip and root end of each blade to keep the covering in place. CyA glue is best for this: Apply a thin coating to all visible wood to harden it, and attach the covering at the same time.

When your heli's blades are in place and properly covered, take a few minutes to be sure they are balanced. Rest the flybar on two cans or similar objects of the same height. Add tape to the tip of the high blade until the rotor head remains level (FIG. 4-13).

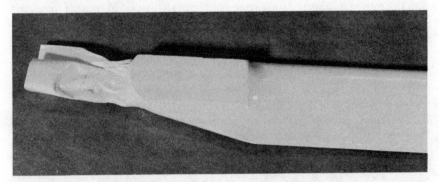

4-12 You can use heat-shrink tubing to cover wooden rotor blades, By pulling on the tubing while shrinking it, you can neatly cover the blade root.

4-13 Balance the rotor blades by resting the flybar on two cans or similar level objects. Add tape to the tip of the high blade until the rotor head is level.

CANOPY PREPARATION

The amount of work involved in preparing the canopy varies from kit to kit. The ones requiring the least work have canopies that are injection-molded or blow-molded, made of either a hard plastic like styrene, or a soft plastic similar to a bleach bottle. A clear windshield is often added to this type of canopy. The ARF helicopters generally use this construction.

Since the canopy is molded of colored plastic, you don't have to paint it. Self-adhesive decals are usually included with the kit to add some color. Just follow the instructions for proper placement of the decals, add the windshield if necessary, and the canopy is finished.

The more traditional kits use a vacuum-formed canopy, which usually has to be trimmed to the proper outline (FIG. 4-14). The exact materials

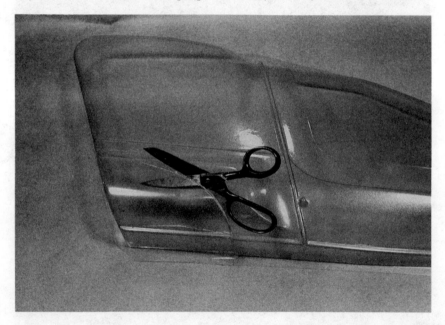

4-14 You must trim vacuum-formed canopies to the proper outline. A scissor works well, but to avoid distortion don't use the very tip of the scissor. In this picture of a Schluter Magic canopy, a cutout is being made to clear the muffler.

vary between manufacturers, but all are similar. The plastic is usually clear or occasionally smoked, so a portion can be masked off before painting to form a windshield. This type of canopy consists of a left half and right half that have to be joined down the middle. A flange is molded in during forming. After the flange is trimmed to a consistent width, the edges to be joined should be sanded to improve adhesion. Then glue the two halves together.

To help hold the two halves together in proper alignment, use small clamps or spring clothespins (FIG. 4-15). If you plan to keep the windshield area clear, use a transparent glue, such as silicone seal, to join the canopy sections. If you will be painting a simulated windshield on the outside,

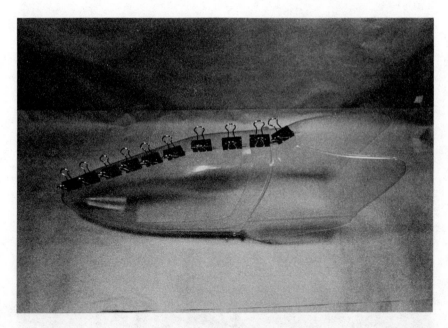

4-15 Spring binder clamps are used to hold the two halves of the canopy together before gluing. You can use clothespins, but the binder clamps work best because of their width and even edges. Make sure the left and right halves are perfectly matched before gluing.

hold the two halves together with clamps first. Then, carefully spread CyA glue on the seam from the inside. The wicking action of the glue will allow it to penetrate the seam.

Canopies formed in clear plastic have to be painted to improve appearance and visibility. You can use spray paint, but it's best to use a fuel-proof paint, like polyurethane enamel.

You can paint either the inside or the outside of a clear canopy. If you plan to use more than one color, it is easier to paint the outside, because the many curves on a helicopter canopy make it difficult to mask the inside for different colors of paint.

If you desire a tinted windshield, the easiest way is to get a can of transparent blue paint and spray the inside of each half of the canopy. After joining, the windshield area is covered with tape and paper. Once all the colors have been masked and sprayed, the windshield can be uncovered, revealing a nicely tinted canopy.

One of several methods will be used to hold the canopy in place. Some kits have a track for the canopy to slide onto; others use mounting brackets and thumbscrews. If you have a vacuum-formed canopy, it may snap over a plywood former, using a rubber band to secure it. If screws are used to hold the canopy in place, be sure to use rubber grommets in the holes. Otherwise, the plastic might wear out due to vibration. The rubber grommet will also help stop the screw from coming out by itself.

SERVO TRAYS

Servo trays are made from either wood or plastic (FIGS. 4-16 and 4-17). The plastic ones need little or no assembly, while the wooden ones require much more work.

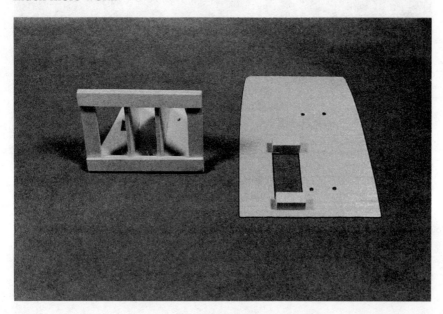

4-16   Completed wooden tray for the GMP Rebel. Upper tray (left) holds the cyclic and tail rotor servos, while the lower tray (right) holds the throttle servo. The lower tray also holds the receiver, battery pack, and gyro.

If your model uses a wooden structure for the radio tray, you'll need some type of glue to hold it together. The two most common adhesives are epoxy and cyanoacrylate glue (CyA). Both work very well.

The CyA can be very convenient because you can "tack" the parts together. *Tack* by using a small amount on each piece and holding them together until the glue sets. You can also use a quick-setting agent on top of the CyA to accelerate the drying time.

Epoxy, on the other hand, requires that you mix two parts to start the curing process, the epoxy and a hardener. Epoxy is available in several set-up times, but the five-minute and twenty-minute varieties are the most widely used. If you are doing this for the first time you might want to use the 20-minute kind so you will have more time to handle the parts before they set up.

Now that you have chosen the adhesive, you can start cutting out the pieces. Most wood kits are die-cut, meaning the wood pieces have an impression outlining them in the wood, and you can push them out with your fingers. Before you do, inspect the grooves to see if they are cleanly cut. You might want to go over them with an X-Acto knife.

If your parts are drawn onto the wood or if you have to trace from a

4-17 Plastic radio trays, like this Kyosho Concept 30 model, require little or no assembly before installing the servos and other radio equipment.

pattern, you will have to saw them out. You can use a jig saw, band saw, scroll saw, or a coping saw.

The pattern should indicate the proper locations for the servos. It is best to set a servo over the pattern and check that the size matches. If it does not, use a pencil to trace the proper outline, centering any extra space on each side.

When using a scroll saw or a jig saw to cut the servo openings, start by drilling a 1/4-inch hole in the center and insert the saw blade into the hole to get a good starting point. When sawing, cut the pieces slightly larger than the outline so you can finish by sanding them smooth.

After all the pieces have been sanded, test-fit them together, making any adjustments necessary for a good fit. When you are satisfied with the fit, you are ready to bond them together.

Using the chosen adhesive, assemble the pieces and set them aside to dry. Once they are dry, check for any spaces between the corners and fill them with the adhesive. Sand the entire structure to prepare for fuel-proofing; a spray can of flat-black paint gives satisfactory results in a short amount of time. The flat finish helps to hide the wood grain, thus requiring less sanding and filling.

RADIO INSTALLATION

Now that the majority of the helicopter assembly is completed, it's time to install the radio. The best place to start is with the servos.

Servo installation

To help isolate vibration, rubber grommets, usually included with the radio's accessory package, are used when mounting the servos. If the grommets are round, they should be pushed through the servo mounting lugs from the top or side. Some servos come with specially molded grommets, which are square. These are installed from the edge by pushing the center part through the opening in the edge of the servo mounting lug. With either type of grommet, you should insert a brass eyelet or bushing in the center of the grommet to prevent the mounting screw from crushing the grommet. If the grommet is crushed, it will do very little to dampen vibration.

Mounting screws are generally provided with the radio, and the helicopter kit might also include some. Whichever ones you use, be sure that the head of the screw is large enough to prevent the servo from coming off. Most mounting screws that come with radios have enlarged heads, similar to a washer, to prevent this problem. If yours don't, you can use a small washer with each screw to be safe.

If you are working with a wooden servo tray, make sure the cutouts for the servos are large enough to prevent the wood from touching the servo case at any point. If it does, any vibration in the radio tray goes directly to the servo, in spite of the rubber mounting. Plastic trays generally have oversized openings to accommodate any size servo, but it's still worth checking for clearance.

Receiver installation

The receiver is the most delicate part of the radio system. It contains a crystal that can be easily damaged by excessive vibration or the impact of even a minor crash. To protect the receiver, wrap it in foam. Carpet padding works quite well for this, but special foam padding is also available at most hobby shops. The foam padding should be wrapped around all sides of the receiver and held in place with electrical tape. Be careful not to wrap too tightly with the tape, or some of the shock absorbency of the foam will be lost (FIG. 4-18).

The airborne power switch should be mounted where it is easy to reach without having to remove the canopy. If the radio tray on your helicopter is made of wood, it will probably have a rear wall that can be used to mount the switch. Cut a hole in the wood to make room for the slide part of the switch, and drill two holes to line up with mounting screws.

You could mount the switch on the side of the tray if there is an opening in the side of the canopy. If there is an open window in the front of the canopy, mount the switch where it can be reached through the window. You can cut a small square opening in the side of the canopy to match up with the most convenient mounting location.

The battery pack should be protected in the same manner as the receiver. Although it is not as sensitive, it is still possible for one of the wires to break off at the solder joint holding it to the cells.

4-18 Use foam padding to protect the receiver, battery pack, and gyro amplifier to isolate vibration and possibly prevent damage in a crash. The Kalt Enforcer shown here uses a rubber band and hooks on the plastic tray to secure the radio equipment. The foam padding is evident.

Once the receiver and battery pack are wrapped in foam, they can be installed in the helicopter. The battery pack should be as far forward on the radio tray as practical to help with the proper balance of the helicopter. Use rubber bands to hold the battery and receiver in place; it is best to use a few extra ones, just in case. Try not to crush the foam, but be sure that neither part can move far enough to pull out a plug. Losing battery power in flight could easily cause a fly-away.

Mounting the gyro

The main part of the gyro, which houses the motor and sensor, must be carefully mounted to function properly. It must be isolated from vibration, but also be able to sense the slightest rotation of the helicopter. The best way to mount the gyro is with several layers of servo mounting tape. The total thickness should be between $1/8$ and $3/16$ inch. If the gyro is mounted too firmly, engine vibration will cause the gyro to make unwanted corrections, causing the tail of the heli to swing occasionally for no obvious reason. If the gyro is mounted so loosely that it can wobble, you will get unwanted corrections as the gyro continues to rotate after you have spun the heli around.

Mount the gyro with the base perpendicular to the main shaft. If the gyro is tilted in any way, either aileron or elevator movements (explained later) will have a small effect on the gyro, causing unwanted tail rotor movements.

The gyro will work no matter how it is rotated on the mounting plate. The instructions included with the gyro show it mounted with the wire lead facing either front or back, and this tends to work best because it puts the gyro motor shaft across the heli so there is less chance of a strong elevator input causing the gyro motor to tilt. Nonetheless, if you aren't satisfied with your gyro performance, don't be afraid to try a different mounting position or method.

The control box can be mounted anywhere the wires will reach. It should be given the same care as the receiver. Ideally, it should be wrapped in foam for protection, then held on with rubber bands. However, with small helicopters, there might not be room for foam around the control box. In such a case, servo tape mounting will have to do.

If your gyro has a separate switch or switch/sensitivity adjustment box, it should be mounted the same way as the receiver switch. If there is room to mount it where it is easily reached, you will want to do so. Otherwise, it too can be mounted anywhere the wires will reach. The trim panel on the front can be used as template if you must cut a hole in plywood to mount it.

CONTROL RODS

Once the complete radio system is installed and operating, you must connect the servos to the control systems of the helicopter. This involves using control rods, or *pushrods*, to transfer the motion of the servo to the appropriate bellcrank, pitch-change arm, or throttle arm. Generally these rods are included in the kit and come cut to length with threads on each end, but they might use a Z-bend on one end instead. *Clevises* or ball links are threaded onto each end of the rods, as needed. Once all the rods are in place, adjust to the proper length and choose the proper hole on the servo arm.

The cyclic controls are the easiest to hook up. They involve the fore and aft, and lateral cyclic controls, which are used to control the tilt of the helicopter; in fixed-wing terms, these are the *aileron* and *elevator* controls respectively. The main concerns are centering and the amount of control movement.

Start by leveling the swashplate. In this position, the helicopter should remain fairly motionless in flight. With the radio turned on and all controls and trims set to neutral, adjust each pushrod so its clevis fastens onto the servo without tilting the swashplate.

Once both servos are connected, check the amount of swashplate tilt that results from full transmitter stick movement. Twenty degrees of tilt in each direction from center should be an acceptable starting point. If it tilts too far, move the pushrod(s) closer to the center of the servo arm. On the other hand, if there is not enough movement at the swashplate, move the pushrod out at the servo. End-point adjustment and dual rates on the radio, if so equipped, will have an effect on this, but do not use them until the basic mechanical adjustments are correct. You can use these features later for minor changes during a flying session.

The next servo to hook up is the tail rotor servo, which controls the yaw of the helicopter. (In fixed-wing terms, it is called the rudder control.) Usually all you need to do is put a clevis on each end of a long pushrod and connect it from the servo at the front to the tail rotor pitch control bellcrank at the back. You may use a joiner in the rod partway back, depending on the brand of helicopter. Some other brands use a wire or stiff cable running inside a plastic tube.

With the servo at neutral, the pushrod should be adjusted to hold the tail rotor blades at the proper angle for stationary flight. To counteract the torque reaction of the main rotor, the tail rotor blades need to be set at approximately a 10-degree angle. The kit directions should show the correct orientation.

Once the pushrod is connected, check the amount of travel available by moving the control stick on the transmitter. There should be no binding of the controls at either extreme. A 10- to 15-degree movement in each direction measured at the tail blade should be sufficient.

With a typical clockwise-rotating main rotor, moving the rudder control all the way to the left will give near zero pitch at the tail. Releasing the rudder stick will give 10 degrees of pitch, and full right will give 20 degrees. (This is not considering the "revolution mixing" that will be added later.) These preliminary settings should be made with the mixing turned off or with the throttle always at the middle position.

If you are using a helicopter radio, you can now adjust the revolution mixing. As the throttle is increased above half stick, the tail rotor pitch should increase at least 5 degrees. Below half stick, it should decrease until it is near zero pitch. You'll make final adjustments after test flying your model.

Hook up the throttle control next, following the same procedure as with previous controls. The exact amount of travel is more important, though. At the full-throttle position, the barrel of the carburetor should be fully opened, but there should be no strain on the throttle arm from the pushrod trying to open it farther. At low throttle, with the throttle trim also at low, the barrel should be fully closed, again with no strain on the arm caused by the servo trying to move it farther than is possible.

With the throttle trim advanced to its middle position, the barrel of the carburetor should be opened far enough to allow the engine to idle. The position of the throttle trim lever will be changed as needed when starting and stopping the engine.

One other consideration when working with the throttle control is what position the arm is in at half throttle. As a starting point, it should be in the middle of its travel. After flight testing, you might find that more or less throttle opening is necessary to allow the helicopter to hover at half stick on the transmitter.

Start adjusting the throttle pushrod by setting the throttle servo and throttle arm to their middle positions. Adjust the length of the pushrod to match the distance between the arms. Next, connect the pushrod to the throttle arm and move it to full throttle. Using the transmitter, put the servo at full throttle. Connect the clevis to whichever hole in the servo arm matches at this position. Now move the transmitter stick to low throttle and check to see if the throttle arm is also at the proper position. If not, adjust the length of the pushrod slightly, or choose a different hole in the servo arm. Be sure to check low-, half-, and full-throttle positions after any change is made.

If you have a fixed pitch helicopter, the controls are all connected. With a collective pitch helicopter, the most important control remains: The collective pitch control must be adjusted properly to get the desired performance from your helicopter. Set full pitch to match the power of the engine. Set the pitch setting at half throttle to give the proper rotor speed during a hover. Finally, set low pitch to give the desired rate of descent during a landing.

The hovering pitch setting is the most important adjustment, so this is where you should start. The instructions that came with your helicopter should tell you what the initial settings should be. If not, a good starting point is as follows.

- For .30 size helicopters, 6 degrees pitch.
- For .50 size helis, 5 degrees pitch.
- For .60 size, 4 degrees pitch.

A pitch gauge should be used to check the blade angle during the adjustments (FIG. 4-19).

4-19 To use the Schluter pitch gauge, or similar gauges, adjust the gauge to be parallel with the flybar. The pointer will indicate the angle of the blade in degrees.

With the transmitter on and the stick in the half-throttle position, adjust the length of the collective pushrod to get the desired hovering pitch setting. When this is correct, check the full power setting. Three degrees more than the hovering pitch setting is a good starting point. Do not make any changes yet; just check the current setting on the helicopter.

Next, check the low pitch setting. Negative 1 degree pitch works well for learning to hover but, with more experience, this can be increased to negative 2 or more. Compare the current setting with the desired setting. If both the low and high settings are insufficient, move the collective pitch control rod out farther from the center of the servo arm. If both settings are larger than desired, move the rod closer to the center of the servo arm.

If only one setting is too large or small, you'll need to use differential movement in the servo arm. *Differential* means that the rod will move farther in one direction than the other. This can be accomplished by lifting the servo arm off the output shaft, rotating it one or two splines, and putting it back on. The arm should be rotated in the direction that needs less travel so the control rod will start to move sideways instead of front to back on one end of its travel. Once this is done, you must adjust the half-throttle setting again.

With a radio that has high- and/or low-pitch adjustment, these settings can be accomplished by using the appropriate controls on the transmitter. It is still best to get the initial settings close mechanically before using the electronic controls to fine-tune the settings.

BALANCE

As a last step, it is a good idea to check the fore and aft balance of the helicopter. Turn the rotor blades till they are facing front to back, placing the flybar across the helicopter. Pick up the helicopter by each side of the flybar, as close to the center as possible. As you lift the helicopter, the nose should hang slightly lower than the tail (FIG. 4-20). The easiest way to

4-20 To check the fore and aft balance, lift your helicopter by the flybar. The helicopter should hang with the nose slightly down, as shown in this picture of a Kalt Enforcer.

tell is to watch whether the front or back of the skids lift off the table first. A 2- to 5-degree nose-low attitude is desirable because it helps give the helicopter a tendency to go forward. As you learn forward flight, the balance will become more important.

Chapter **5**

First flight

*I*n this chapter, we will finally get your helicopter in the air! If you can find help locally, by all means do so. If you must learn on your own, then this chapter should get you started in the right direction. Proceed at a careful pace and you will have the best results.

STARTING EQUIPMENT

First, we will review what equipment will be needed to fly the helicopter. The following six items will be necessary to start the engine.

1. Glow plug for the engine
2. 1.5-volt battery, or power panel and glow plug leads
3. Fuel
4. Fuel pump
5. Electric starter with adapter if needed
6. 12-volt battery for starter and/or power panel

All glow engines require glow fuel. Glow fuel is comprised of two main components, methyl alcohol and a lubricant. The two most widely used lubricants in today's fuels are castor oil and synthetic oil. There are many arguments as to which lubricant or combinations of lubricants are the best. One could devote several pages of information on the subject and only scratch the surface, so the best bet is to check with your local hobby store to see what they recommend or what other pilots are using in their helicopters.

If you are unable to obtain assistance in this fashion, check the mail-order houses and order the helicopter blend. As I mentioned in chapter 3, the heli blends are usually darker in color than aircraft fuel to make it easier to visually check the fuel level.

Most fuels also include nitro-methane and indicate the amount in percentages, like 10 percent. Nitro provides some extra power and an improvement in throttle response, but too high a nitro content raises the combustion temperature, which can reduce engine life. You don't have to worry unless you are approaching 20 percent nitro content.

A 12-volt motorcycle battery or a 12-volt gel cell with at least a 6-amp rating will be sufficient to turn over all sizes of engines. If you have a flight box built from a kit, it will have a place to store your battery. If you do not have a flight box, you can easily carry a gel cell to the field because it is designed not to spill, no matter how it is carried.

An electric starter with the correct starting attachment is necessary to turn your engine over and start it. As you've learned, the two methods most commonly used to transfer the starting force are the belt and cone starts. With the belt start, there is no additional equipment needed, but with the cone start, an extension to reach the cone is required, so be sure you have one. Another word to the wise: The hex drive provides a no-slip connection between the starter and the engine; however, hex-drive start systems can be added at any time as an after-market product, but their use can void some manufacturers' warranties. Be sure to check before making modifications.

A glow driver uses a 1.5-volt battery to ignite the glow plug during starting procedures. Once started, you remove this device as the engine produces enough heat to continue the glow. There are different types of glow drivers—some using replaceable batteries, while others are permanently sealed. An adapter for recharging the battery is either included or available separately.

A power panel is an integral part of a good flight box and may also be used to light a glow plug. Power panels drop the 12-volt input power down to 1−2 volts or send pulses to the glow plug that average out to 1−2 volts. A rheostat provides a means of adjustment to control the power. Most power panels also provide power for an electric fuel pump.

TRAINING

Several aids are available for the learning pilot that will save you many hours of frustration—not to mention many dollars in repair bills. These aids come in the form of test stands or training gear. Let's look at the test stands first.

Test stands

The simplest form of a stand is simply to tether your helicopter to a stationary object, like a heavy table. The biggest drawback to this kind of stand is that the conditions are very unrealistic. The only positive aspect is that you cannot crash—as long as you have firmly fixed your helicopter to the table. You can make carb adjustments, but they will change when the helicopter isn't trying to airlift the picnic table into the neighbor's yard!

Commercial test stands are expensive in cost initially, but when you think about the cost of a couple of mishaps, they are worth considering. These stands allow the helicopter a good deal of freedom without jeopardy. You can practice vertical, horizontal, and rotational movements (albeit only in the radius limits of the stand). You can also use such stands at a later date to learn more advanced maneuvers like nose-in hovering.

Training gear

Most new pilots opt for a simple form of training gear, fashioned from wooden dowels and whiffle balls.

Several configurations using the dowels are possible. The recommended size is 3/8-inch diameter and the dowels should be approximately the same as the rotor diameter. You can lay two dowels along the skids and two perpendicular to the first dowels. Using wire ties, fasten them together in a tic-tac-toe arrangement. Fasten the grid work to the landing skids with rubber bands (#64) and away you go!

Using two dowels and four whiffle balls, you can make training gear that can slide around on a smooth surface such as asphalt or short grass (FIG. 5-1). Fasten the dowels perpendicular to each other with a whiffle ball

5-1   The training gear on this Schluter Junior 50 will help to prevent accidental tipovers while learning. The whiffle balls allow the helicopter to slide on the ground, making it easier to learn control directions in the early stages of learning.

at each end. Make such the whiffle ball is restricted along the dowels but also that it rotates freely. Attach the gear to the landing skids, and you are ready to start. This type of training gear is the most popular, and several manufacturers even package all the needed parts together as a kit (FIG. 5-2).

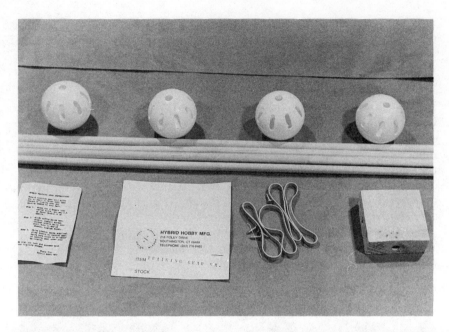

5-2 Training gear, such as this from Hybrid Hobby Mfg., is invaluable when you're learning to fly RC helicopters.

The advantage to using training gear is a totally free-moving model. Let's face it—sooner or later, your bird has to get into the air by itself and if you cannot afford a training stand, this is the safest way to do it. You will be limited only by your ability to confine the model. Make sure you have plenty of open area while learning with training gear.

RADIO CHECKOUT

If you are at a club field or place where other RC flyers gather, check with the other pilots or with the frequency control board to see if your channel is clear. Once you are sure it is, turn on your transmitter, then turn on your receiver and your gyro (if so equipped). Operate all functions on the transmitter and watch for the proper response from your helicopter.

With the antenna collapsed, walk away from your helicopter while moving the sticks. Watch for the point where the control response becomes erratic. This is called a *range check*. When you have walked 50–60 feet away, you should still be able to detect control surfaces moving correctly. If your antenna collapses completely inside the transmitter, 15 feet of range is acceptable. The purpose of this test is to verify the performance of the radio system. Repeat it at the start of each flying session. If you notice a sudden decrease in range, see that the radio system is serviced by a qualified service center right away.

With the antenna extended and the helicopter airborne, the range of the radio system will easily exceed your ability to see the model. Most radio manufacturers claim an airborne range of at least 3,500 feet.

Just to play it safe, check all the control directions one more time. As you push the right transmitter stick forward, the swashplate should tilt forward. As you push the same stick to the right, the swashplate should tilt right. (Some Schluter helicopter models are an exception to this. Their instructions explain the differences.)

Pushing the left stick forward should increase throttle. The collective pitch should also increase, if so equipped. Moving the same stick to the right should increase pitch in the tail rotor (compared to the hover setting for a clockwise-rotating helicopter).

STARTING

After you fill the fuel tank, hook up your starter to the 12-volt power source. Check the trim settings on the transmitter, making sure the throttle stick is at the low position and the hi idle and throttle hold switches are off. (You might even want to inhibit these functions until you are ready to use them.) Put the throttle trim to the halfway point so the engine will be able to idle.

Connect the glow plug power source and engage the electric starter. Be sure to keep one hand on the rotor head in case the engine starts at a higher speed than expected (FIG. 5-3).

The engine should turn over and start fairly quickly. If the engine does not start within 20 seconds, increase the throttle trim slowly until the engine starts. If this does not help, try opening the needle valve further. If

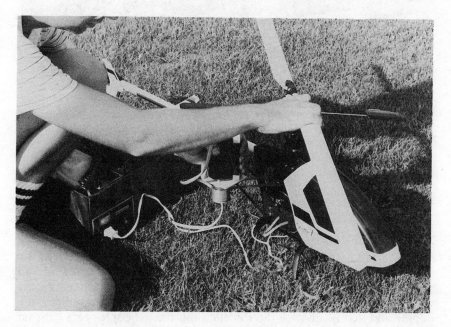

5-3 Proper starting procedure for belt-start helicopters, like this Shuttle ZX. As a safety measure, keep one hand on the rotor head while starting the engine. Make sure the throttle stick is set low before starting.

you continue to have trouble starting the engine, refer to chapter 7. Once started, remove the starter and allow the engine to idle for 5 or 10 seconds before removing the glow plug connector.

NEEDLE VALVE

It can be difficult at first to properly adjust the high-speed needle valve (FIG. 5-4). With a helicopter, the rotor blades start to spin as soon as the throttle is advanced. The hover settings can also be complicated because most flying is done at half throttle, where both the main and idle mixture settings have an effect. As a novice pilot, you might have an especially difficult time since you are not yet prepared to use full throttle for even a short time. One way around some of these problems is to fasten the helicopter to a test stand to make the adjustments, but this will not fully duplicate the changing loads that are put on the engine in flight.

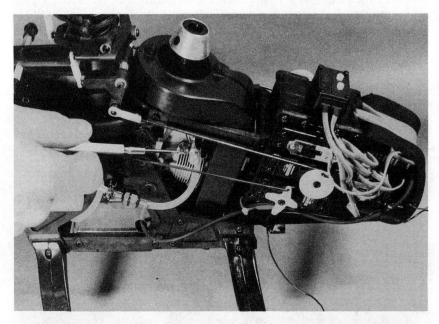

5-4 The high speed (main) needle valve adjustment is usually located on the same side of the carburetor as the fuel tube connection.

Your main concern at this time, however, is that the engine runs well enough to learn how to hover. As you become more experienced, the "perfect setting" becomes more important. The best way to start out with a new helicopter and engine is to open the needle valve at least as far as the instructions recommend, usually three to four turns. Start the engine and slowly advance the throttle until the helicopter gets light on its skids. At this point there should be a fair amount of smoke and the rotor rpm should be at the proper speed. If there is not enough smoke, open the needle valve and try it again.

When you start out there will probably be plenty of smoke, but it will take full throttle to get the helicopter to lift off. If this is the case, turn the needle valve in several clicks and run up the engine again. The goal is to have the helicopter start to lift off the ground at approximately half throttle and to have a steady stream of smoke. If there is not enough smoke, the engine will overheat from being too lean and will eventually lose power or quit.

Adjusting the idle mixture can be even more complicated (FIG. 5-5). When learning to hover, the idle mixture setting is not that important. As long as the engine will idle for a minute or two, don't worry about it. If the engine slows down during an idle before quitting, try leaning out the idle. If, on the other hand, there is a brief increase in speed before quitting, try richening the idle mixture.

5-5 The idle mixture needle valve is often located in the center of the throttle arm. Consult the engine instructions for more details on the particular engine that you have chosen.

BLADE TRACKING

One of the first things to check when trimming out a helicopter is the rotor blade tracking. The first step is to observe which blade is higher. Colored tape on the tip of one of the blades will help to determine which blade is which. Add throttle until the helicopter is light on its skids, then bend over and look at the blades from the side. If you can see that both blades are not running at the same height, you'll need to adjust the tracking.

Reduce the throttle to idle and wait for the blades to stop. To lower the high blade, you must reduce the pitch, or angle of attack. With a helicopter that has collective pitch control, you must adjust one of the ball links on the rotor head. Starting at the blade holder control ball link, follow the rods back to the first place that has a threaded ball link—this might be directly at the blade holder, or farther down through the mixing levers. To lower the blade, pull down the leading edge or push up the trailing edge, depending on whether the connection at the blade holder is located at the front or back of the blade. Try one-half or one full turn at a time, depending on the type of ball links and how serious the problem is.

With a fixed pitch helicopter, the blade tracking is adjusted by bending one of the blade holders to raise or lower the pitch angle. Either increase pitch on the low blade to raise it, or decrease pitch on the high blade to lower it. Two adjustable wrenches work well for doing this. Use one wrench on the blade holder at the blade, the other on the rotor head to prevent it from moving.

STATIONARY HOVER

As you advance the throttle, the helicopter might rotate until the rotor speed becomes stabilized. Continue to add throttle until the helicopter is light on its skids. If the helicopter continues to rotate at this point, you will have to adjust the tail rotor control. Most helicopters have a clockwise rotating rotor head, so we will assume that is the case. If you have a model with a counterclockwise rotation, then reverse the following directions.

If the nose of the helicopter turns to the left (when viewed from behind), increase the amount of positive pitch in the tail rotor, thereby increasing the amount of thrust produced by the tail rotor. The tail of the helicopter will move toward the left, moving the nose to the right, and canceling out the left turn.

If the nose of the helicopter wants to turn to the right, then reduce the pitch of the tail blades in order to cause the tail rotor to produce less thrust. This will allow the torque caused by the main blades to rotate the nose of the helicopter toward the left, canceling out the right turn tendency.

There might be one or more ways to adjust the tail rotor pitch on your helicopter, depending on the model. You can always make minor adjustments at the transmitter using the rudder trim. You can adjust the pushrod connection at the rudder servo to eliminate an off-center condition of the rudder trim.

Larger changes can also be made at the servo, if needed. When doing so, check the pushrod movement at full left and right control. There should be no binding at the extremes; if there is, you might have to make your adjustments elsewhere. You can also adjust the pushrod connection at the tail rotor control bellcrank with similar results.

Some helicopter designs have an adjustment for tail rotor pitch at the pitch change plate. This is the type that has the blade pitch controlled by a wire passing through the tail rotor shaft. A plate is held on the wire by two collars, one on each side. Ball links are fastened from the plate to the tail rotor blade holders. By moving the collars in or out, the blade pitch can be changed without affecting the movement of the servo, pushrod, or bellcrank. With this type of design, you should adjust the bellcrank to move equally in each direction, then adjust the pitch change plate so the tail blades have the proper pitch for a stationary hover.

If the helicopter constantly tries to move left, right, front, or back, the cyclic controls, found on the right stick of the transmitter, must be adjusted. They directly control the tilt of the swashplate, which controls the tilt and movement of the helicopter.

If the helicopter constantly moves forward or backward, you must adjust the elevator trim. The trim should be adjusted gradually in a direction opposite to the way the helicopter is moving. If the helicopter is moving forward, move the trim back, toward the up elevator direction. This will raise the nose of the helicopter, stopping it from moving forward. If the helicopter moves to the rear, then down elevator trim should be used to correct the situation.

If the model moves to the left or right, aileron correction is necessary. Slowly move the trim lever in the direction needed to counteract the movement of the helicopter. Moving the trim to the right will stop the helicopter from going to the left, and vice versa.

Once the helicopter is trimmed for a stationary hover, the trims on the transmitter can be recentered by adjusting the lengths of the pushrods at the servos to get the same swashplate position after the trims have been moved back to neutral. Do not set the transmitter trims back to center between flights: Once they are adjusted properly, don't change them unless the pushrods are readjusted or the helicopter shows the need for further trimming.

TAIL ROTOR MIXING

If the helicopter does not rotate during a hover, but tries to turn at other throttle positions, then you must adjust the tail rotor mixing, called *revolution mixing* on most radios and *tail rotor compensation* on others. Until you are able to fly the helicopter, it will be very difficult to adjust the tail rotor mixing correctly. As you learn to fly, you might want to come back to this section. The following directions should give you a suitable starting point.

To check the mixing direction, adjust the tail rotor pitch to maintain a stationary hover. This will call for 10 to 15 degrees of pitch in the tail rotor blades. Make sure it is the right direction. If it is wrong the helicopter will spin quickly in a direction opposite that of the main rotors. Now start out with the throttle stick at the half position. Make sure the mixing knobs are adjusted higher than zero so some mixing will be evident. Slowly increase the throttle stick, and observe the movement of the tail rotor blades. As the throttle is increased, the tail rotor blades should increase in pitch to compensate for the increased pitch in the main blades. As the throttle is reduced, the tail rotor pitch should move toward zero pitch. At low throttle, the tail rotor blades should have little or no angle of attack.

If the nose of the helicopter rotates to the left as full throttle is applied, then more compensation is required. The up mixing knob should be turned toward a higher setting. If the nose of the helicopter turns toward the right at full throttle, then the mixing should be reduced. Turn the up mixing knob to a lower setting.

If the nose of the helicopter turns toward the left when the throttle is reduced below hover, you need to decrease the down mixing. This will be most easily observed during a landing approach. If the nose moves to the right when the throttle is reduced below half stick, the compensation should be decreased. Turn the down mixing knob to a lower setting.

If you are not successful in adjusting the mixing circuit, make sure it is working in the correct direction. Some radios have a switch to set the direction, others allow the adjustment knobs to control the direction, with zero mix in the middle of its range of movement. One or two radios on the market do not offer a way to change the mixing direction; they assume a standard setup with a clockwise rotor head.

GYRO ADJUSTMENT

To get the most benefit a gyro has to offer, you'll want to adjust the sensitivity to suit your skill level and personal preference. This is strictly a trial-and-error procedure. Starting from the basic 50-percent setting, test-fly the helicopter and see how the tail rotor response is. The helicopter should have a "locked in" feeling, but should also allow you enough control response to do what you want.

If the sensitivity is set too low, you won't be receiving the full benefit of the gyro. If the setting is too high, the tail will wag back and forth rhythmically. If you want more pilot-control authority, the sensitivity can be turned down a little bit at a time. Alternatively, the control throw going to the tail rotor can be increased at the servo. If the transmitter is equipped with end-point adjustment or dual rates, you might be able to use them to increase control sensitivity. If you increase control throw at the servo, the effectiveness of the gyro will be increased. Most likely, the sensitivity will have to be decreased slightly to make allowance for it.

If the gyro you have chosen is equipped with two sensitivity control pots, they are selectable at the transmitter by using a spare channel to control it. Most pilots use the retract channel, but any channel controlled by a switch will do. One setting is used for normal flying, with the other setting being reserved for special maneuvers like a 540-degree stall turn or a fast pirouette. Some pilots choose to use one setting for hovering and the other for forward flight. The choice is yours.

Chapter **6**

Flight training

At this point, I'll assume that you have a helicopter that is properly adjusted. As you progress through the training exercises, you might find things that should be changed in the helicopter setup. If so, please refer to earlier chapters or consult chapter 7 for troubleshooting suggestions.

First, a few words of advice. The quickest way to learn to fly a radio control helicopter is to go slowly. If you push yourself too far beyond your present abilities, a crash is inevitable. Time that could have been spent practicing with your helicopter will have to be spent on repairs. After the helicopter is repaired, you'll have to devote even more time to adjusting the helicopter to match its previous trim settings. Don't allow yourself to be tempted or persuaded to show off for spectators while you are still learning to fly.

HOVERING

Every helicopter flight starts and ends in a stationary hover. (The exception is a flight that ends in a crash, but we've already decided to avoid that.) On your first attempts, the hover duration will be only a few seconds. Your goal is to be able to hold the helicopter in a stationary hover indefinitely. **Note:** Don't let this goal get in the way of learning. You might find yourself tempted to try to keep the helicopter in the air as long as possible, gauging your progress by the duration of the hover. If you use this approach, you'll have to perform every landing as an emergency maneuver to avoid crashing.

A much better way to learn to hover is to concentrate on controlled landings. Lift the helicopter off the ground, hold it stationary for a second or two, then practice making a smooth, controlled descent to a landing. By practicing smooth landings first, you'll develop reflexes that will allow you to land safely later on when things go a little bit wrong.

During the first stages of learning, stand behind the helicopter and a little bit to either side to get a better view. From this position, you'll be less likely to get the controls confused. Position the helicopter with the nose pointed into the wind: the helicopter will have a tendency to turn into the wind, so you might as well start out there.

The first control to practice is the throttle (and collective pitch). Slowly add throttle until the helicopter is light on its skids; you know you have reached this point when one or more legs of the training gear momentarily lift off the ground. At this point, add the slightest bit more throttle. The helicopter should slowly rise. At an altitude of three to six inches, gently pull the throttle stick back. The helicopter should settle softly to the ground. Continue to practice this until you can consistently land the helicopter smoothly every time.

As you become familiar with the other controls, you'll be able to fly the helicopter safely at a higher altitude. As you progress, come back to this step and practice landing from a greater height. When you feel you are ready, gradually increase your maximum altitude to one or two feet. As you descend from this higher altitude, you will find that it is necessary to add throttle again, just before touchdown, to cushion the landing. Continue to practice landings until you feel that you have full control of the landing speed.

Now that you know how to use the throttle stick to control the altitude of the helicopter, you need to become familiar with the other controls. You can get a feel for each control without letting the helicopter get more than a few inches off the ground. Gradually increase the throttle until the helicopter gets light on its skids. Experiment with each directional control one at a time—the tail rotor control is a good place to start.

Practice rotating the helicopter from side to side. At this point, you will notice that the controls are sluggish as long as the training gear are touching the ground. Once completely clear of the ground, the helicopter is free to move much faster. Keep this in mind as you gain confidence and start to fly higher.

Continue to familiarize yourself with the controls by experimenting with the right stick. As long as you stand behind the helicopter, the helicopter will move in whatever direction you move the control stick. Start by allowing the helicopter to slide along the ground. (Eventually you might want to steer the helicopter along a predetermined course to force yourself to use the controls, rather than just letting the helicopter wander.) Then move the helicopter forward, backward, left, and right.

You should be able to control the altitude and direction of the helicopter before you move on to holding the helicopter stationary over one spot. Start with a short duration hover, around five seconds or so. Try one or two directional inputs, then land before you get in trouble. Gradually increase the duration of the hover, but try to land before things go wrong so you avoid slamming the helicopter into the ground in a panic.

As your skills continue to improve, gradually increase the altitude of the hover. With each increase in height, temporarily return to a shorter duration hover. Continue to practice until you can hold the helicopter at a consistent altitude without drifting away from the starting point.

At this point, you are ready to start moving the helicopter around in a more deliberate manner. You will accomplish two things by doing this. First, you will learn to move the helicopter where you want and to stop it at that spot. Second, you will learn to control the helicopter from a varying perspective.

Up until now, you have been standing behind the helicopter while flying it. As you start to move the helicopter around more, you will see the sides and eventually the front of the helicopter. You might find this a little disconcerting at first because you can't just move the control stick in the direction you want the helicopter to move. Instead you have to learn to work the controls as if you were actually sitting in the helicopter. For example, while left cyclic control input always makes the helicopter go to its left, it might not always be to *your* left, depending on where you are standing and which way the helicopter is facing.

Start by slipping the helicopter sideways away from you. This will take lateral cyclic (aileron) control in the desired direction. You might want to use a little bit of opposite tail rotor to counteract the "weathervaning" tendency of the helicopter. Move it sideways for five or ten feet, then stop and slip back toward yourself. If all is going well, you can continue on to the other side so you'll get a chance to see each side of the helicopter while it is flying.

When you become comfortable with this, start to add some tail rotor control in the same direction as the helicopter is side-slipping to aim the helicopter in the direction that it is moving. Once it is headed away from you, release the tail rotor control and allow it to continue in a straight line. When you reach the point where you want to stop, use a little bit of back stick to slow down the helicopter. Before the heli comes to a stop, use opposite cyclic (aileron) and tail rotor (rudder) to turn the helicopter around and head it back toward you.

Until you are able to fly the helicopter looking at the nose from an angle, you can side-slip the helicopter back toward you. Eventually you will be able to make the heli fly away to either side, make a smooth turn with the tail rotor, and fly back to you. Continue past and make a turn on the other side, and you have a *figure eight*. This is an excellent way to learn all the controls on the helicopter, as well as becoming comfortable with seeing the helicopter from different angles. Other maneuvers you can practice at this point include figure eights with the nose headed into the wind, and tail-in circles around yourself.

To do the figure eight, start with the helicopter headed into the wind. Drift forward slightly, then start to either side. Change to some back stick to drift rearward, then switch to opposite lateral cyclic to drift back toward center. Continue toward center, moving forward to and beyond the original starting point. Go around the circle on the other side, coming back to the starting point, and then land. This will teach you to use all the controls in a very deliberate manner.

The tail-in circle maneuver allows you to use the tail rotor control more. Lift off headed into the wind, then start side-slipping to either side. Use tail rotor control in the same direction as cyclic to make the helicopter turn around yourself. If you are flying under windy conditions, use the tail rotor control in varying amounts as you go from headwind to cross-wind to tailwind. At some points you will need a lot of tail rotor input; at other points you'll need practically none.

Once you can do a tail-in circle, try adding more tail rotor control to turn the nose toward the direction the helicopter is moving. You will get a chance to see the helicopter from the side, and get a feel for what it is like to have the helicopter moving forward. Continue to circle around yourself, with the nose pointing more and more into the direction of flight. If you become uncomfortable at any point, put the helicopter back into a tail-in circle by using opposite tail rotor.

FORWARD FLIGHT

By the time you are able to fly the helicopter through a slow figure eight, you are very close to taking the next big step, moving into forward flight. The hardest part of forward flight is the transition back to a hover. To practice, continue with the figure eights, but as you fly away to the side, add more throttle so the helicopter climbs slowly. After you have turned around, reduce the throttle to start a gentle descent. If the helicopter drops too quickly, add some throttle again.

As the helicopter approaches you, slow the forward speed by pulling the right stick back slightly to raise the nose of the helicopter. When it reaches an altitude of three feet or so, add some more throttle to stop the helicopter from dropping any further. At this point, you can practice returning to a hover or continue on to the other side of the figure eight.

To practice landing, bring the helicopter back into a hover, then slowly reduce throttle to land. Be sure to practice landing from both sides whenever conditions permit. When it is windy, you'll want to land with the helicopter headed into the wind; it will be much more stable this way.

Another way to practice landings is to make the heli fly a circle around you. Gradually let the helicopter climb on one side, then drop on the other. When everything goes right, bring the helicopter back into a hover. Gradually increase the size of the circle and the height of the maneuver as your skills increase.

The only problem with circling the helicopter around you is that you are not forced to see all sides of the helicopter; you constantly see the helicopter from the same side. However, it's still a good maneuver to use to practice landing because you are able to keep the helicopter close to you while you're first trying it out.

When you are comfortable bringing the helicopter back into a hover from slow forward flight, it's time to branch out a little bit. Start out with your best maneuver, either a figure eight or circle. Fly several repetitions to get into the swing of things, then gradually increase the distance flown between turns. As the copter flies farther away, increase the altitude. If you are using the circling approach, turn the circle into an oval by stretching each side. When you reach a distance that starts to feel uncomfortable, turn the helicopter around and head back. Make each circuit smaller until you are back to your standard maneuver. From there you should be able to land safely.

As you become more comfortable with forward flight, you will be able to go farther and farther away without losing orientation. If you have trouble at any time recognizing what the helicopter is doing, just tell yourself that it must be doing what it should be. If you are turning, continue through the turn. Within a moment or two, you should be able to recognize the attitude of the helicopter again. The worst thing to do when you get disoriented is to change what you are doing. Just let the helicopter carry through with what you started and everything should go well.

Eventually you will want to try making different types of landing approaches. If your helicopter has collective pitch, you can perform high-speed approaches by pulling the throttle stick all the way back to get into the negative pitch range. Using an idle-up circuit on the radio will keep the rotor speed up during the landing approach. If your radio does not have idle-up, pushing the throttle trim all the way forward before taking off will serve the same purpose.

When you come in from a high-speed approach, you need to give the helicopter much stronger control inputs to make it stop. Pull the nose up sharply to bleed off the forward speed. To stop the helicopter from hitting the ground, increase the throttle at the bottom of the approach. Remember that as the helicopter comes to a stop, you must put the throttle back to the hover position.

From the beginning, you have been practicing slow landing approaches. Now that you can fly farther away and at a higher altitude, you can perfect your long, slow landing approaches.

Let the helicopter slow down much earlier at altitude. By carefully using the fore and aft cyclic and throttle controls, you can fly the helicopter on a straight-line descent.. If the helicopter slows down too much, drop the nose slightly and advance the throttle to keep moving. This type of landing approach is a good way to become familiar with flying the helicopter while looking at it from the front. If you get into trouble, just drop the nose, increase throttle, and fly the heli past yourself.

ADVANCED HOVERING

After learning to fly around, don't neglect your hovering practice! Many things you will want to learn to do are easier once you have learned to fly around, but one of the most difficult maneuvers is to hover nose-in (looking directly at the front of the helicopter). In this position, the fore-and-aft cyclic, lateral cyclic, and tail rotor controls are reversed compared to viewing the helicopter from the rear. Of course, if you have practiced these controls by thinking of yourself as a pilot in the helicopter, you'll have much less trouble.

Slow pirouettes are one way to learn nose-in flight. Actually, it teaches you two maneuvers at once. At an altitude of at least five feet, slowly give a tail rotor input to rotate the helicopter. If you start to feel uncomfortable, switch the control to the opposite direction to return to tail-in. Stop at various positions during the rotation to become familiar with each view. As you approach the nose-in position, hold it for only a few seconds, then return to tail-in.

While in the nose-in position, try one or two directional control inputs. Remember that while looking at the front of the helicopter, pulling back stick will move the helicopter away from you. If you get in trouble, return to the tail-in position. When you can go beyond the nose-in position, try returning to tail-in by continuing the spin, rather than changing directions. When you can do this smoothly, you have mastered the pirouette.

Another way to learn nose-in hovering is to put the training gear back on, enabling you to practice nose-in flight from takeoff to landing. The training gear should help prevent tipovers, just as they did when you were first learning to hover.

You'll find it much easier to learn difficult hovering maneuvers after learning forward flight because you can always get out of trouble by adding throttle and climbing out. Once the helicopter is up higher, you can sort out the problem, circle around, and return to a hover. Remember: helicopters don't crash going up, only coming down. Once you have the option of climbing up away from trouble, feel free to try any type of hovering maneuver.

AEROBATICS

For some pilots, forward flight is a sufficient accomplishment, but others want to learn aerobatic maneuvers. Once you are capable of doing the basic aerobatics, elements of each maneuver can be combined with others to form new maneuvers.

Stall turn

A stall turn consists of pulling the helicopter into a vertical climb, performing a 180-degree rotation as the helicopter runs out of speed, and then making a vertical dive followed by a pull-out to level flight. When you are first learning the stall turn, don't worry about making the helicopter achieve a true vertical line. A 45-degree climb should be sufficient to get the feel of the maneuver.

Start by putting the helicopter into fast forward flight. As it passes in front of you, pull the nose of the helicopter up into a sharp climb. Reduce the pitch to stop the helicopter from being pulled toward the top. As the helicopter stops climbing, give full tail rotor control to rotate the helicopter. Hold the tail rotor control until the nose is pointed down, then release it and let the helicopter drop nose-down to build up speed. Gradually pull back on the elevator stick until the helicopter is back in a level flight attitude, then add throttle to fly out of the maneuver. Practice the stall turn until you can establish a perfect vertical climb, exactly 180-degree rotation, and a straight dive with a pull-out at the same altitude as the entry.

Loop

Once you have mastered the stall turn, you are ready to try a loop. The entry is the same as a stall turn: start by gently pulling some up elevator to start the loop. Continue pulling up elevator to flip the helicopter over on its back. Reduce the pitch slightly at the top of the loop so the helicopter does not drop as quickly. On the back side of the loop, use full up elevator to finish the loop. At the bottom, exit the loop with the nose slightly low, and add throttle to fly out of it.

Roll

You should have a helicopter with collective pitch to try to perform a roll, and having a helicopter radio will make things much easier. Use the idle up feature to maintain rotor rpm while using negative pitch. At least three degrees of negative pitch should be available at full low stick.

Start the roll by putting the helicopter into fast forward flight. As it passes you, pull the nose up slightly. Go to full right aileron control and hold the stick there. As the helicopter becomes inverted, pull the throttle stick back all the way to get some lift by using negative pitch. Continue rolling through inverted back to upright. As the helicopter approaches upright flight, go back to three-quarter or full throttle to regain lift. If the helicopter lost speed through the roll, drop the nose to accelerate again.

Autorotation

Autorotation could someday save your helicopter. An autorotation, as you know, is a landing without power from the engine. To practice the maneuver, you need a helicopter radio that has a throttle hold switch. The hold switch lets you put the throttle servo in the proper position for a low idle, while still having full control of collective pitch.

Before trying an autorotation, you should be familiar with the high-speed landing approach. The two maneuvers are very similar on the way down. The difference is that the autorotation only allows a second or so to set the helicopter down after stopping the forward movement. Start the descent by pulling the throttle stick back. Use hi-idle to maintain rpm during the first part of the descent; then, once the helicopter has established the desired approach path, turn on the throttle hold switch to drop the engine to an idle. The helicopter should continue the same flight path down toward the landing spot.

By pulling the nose up with a little back stick, you should be able to slow both the descent and the forward speed at the same time. When you are within several feet of the ground, smoothly add pitch to bring the helicopter to a stop. Try not to use more pitch than necessary, so you will have some lift available if needed. If all goes well, the helicopter should settle gently to the ground.

Be careful not to stop the helicopter too high off the ground, or you will run out of rotor speed before landing. Also, make sure the helicopter is level before it touches down. You might have to use a little down elevator to drop the nose before landing if you pulled the nose up sharply during the landing approach. If you hold back elevator all the way to the ground, you will have an unpleasant experience called a *boom strike*, which occurs when the main rotor blades bend down and hit the tailboom. While the helicopter is in the air, back stick tilts the entire craft back. Once the helicopter is on the ground, however, it can't tilt anymore, and back stick will tilt only the rotor disk back. Add to this the downward bounce caused by hitting the ground, even gently, and the blades can swing down and hit the tailboom. Avoid a boom strike by pushing the elevator stick forward to level the helicopter at the last moment.

Chapter 7

Troubleshooting

*T*o solve problems that might occur while learning to fly your helicopter, you need to be able to recognize them. This chapter covers common problems and how to fix them. You might also find relevant advice in the earlier chapters dealing with assembly and radio installation.

ENGINE STARTING PROBLEMS

If the engine turns over but won't start, first check the fuel supply to the carburetor. Make sure all tubing is in order. The main needle valve must be open far enough to allow fuel to reach the engine—anywhere from 1 to 5 turns, depending on the brand of engine. The instructions that came with the engine give you a good starting point.

You should be able to see fuel in the line at the carburetor. If not, you can force it through the line by putting your finger over the exhaust pipe of the muffler and running the engine for a few seconds with the electric starter. You can also pinch the pressure line and squeeze the tank to force fuel to the carburetor.

If you are using muffler pressure, there should be no open lines on the fuel tank. If you are not using pressure, then one line must be open on the tank to prevent a suction from forming as the fuel is used. (Muffler pressure offers the best results.)

The glow plug must be glowing brightly in order for the engine to start. Glow plugs will occasionally burn out, or deteriorate after extended use. Remove the glow plug and hook up the 1.5-volt battery to check the condition of both the plug and battery. If there is only a dim glow, then the battery is probably worn out. If you are using a power panel to light the plug, use the adjustment knob to turn up the power until the plug is bright red. Be careful: too much power will burn it out, so go slowly.

Make sure the electric starter is spinning in the correct direction. The engine, looking from the front, should run counterclockwise. Looking at the end of the starter, it should be spinning clockwise. If this is not the case, reverse the connections at the 12-volt battery.

If the engine fires but will not keep running, there are several possible causes. Check the direction of the starter if you have not already done so. If the needle valve is drastically out of adjustment, the engine could be getting too much or too little fuel to allow it to run. If the fuel is dripping out of the muffler, there is a good chance that the needle valve is open too far. If not, you can try forcing some extra fuel into the engine by putting your finger over the muffler exhaust.

If the engine won't turn over at all, it might be flooded—having excess fuel inside the cylinder. If the fuel tank is higher than the carburetor, fuel can slowly seep into the engine. After long periods of storage, oil residue from the fuel might thicken, making it harder to start the engine. The cure for either problem is to remove the glow plug and use the starter to turn the engine over for a few seconds, clearing out any extra fuel and also making the engine easier to spin. If the engine turns over very slowly, even with the plug out, then the starter battery might be in poor condition. Charge your starter battery regularly.

HOVERING PROBLEMS

If, during a hover, you notice that one rotor blade is not running in line with the other, you must adjust the tracking. First observe which blade is higher, then land the helicopter and wait for the blades to stop. To lower the high blade, you must reduce the pitch.

With a helicopter that has collective pitch control, adjust one of the ball links on the rotor head. Starting at the blade holder control ball link, follow the rods back to the first place that has a threaded ball link. (This might be directly at the blade holder or further down through the mixing levers.) To lower the blade, pull the leading edge down or push the trailing edge up, depending on whether the connection at the blade holder is located at the front or back of the blade. Try one-half or one full turn at a time, depending on the type of ball links, and how serious the problem is.

With a fixed pitch helicopter, adjust the blade tracking by bending one of the blade holders in order to raise or lower the pitch angle. Either increase pitch on the low blade to raise it or decrease pitch on the high blade to lower it. Two adjustable wrenches work well: use one wrench on the blade holder at the blade and the other on the rotor head to prevent it from moving (FIG. 7-1).

If the blade tracking constantly changes, check the helicopter for loose or bent parts. If you have recently crashed the helicopter, you might have overlooked a part that should have been changed. Pay extra attention to the metal parts that support the blade holders. The specifics will vary with the type of rotor head, but each type has one or more parts that could cause an erratic tracking problem.

If there are any loose balls on the rotor head, mixing levers, or swashplate, you can expect to have erratic problems as the ball moves

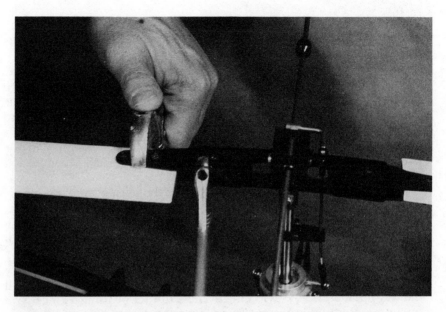

7-1 Blade tracking on a fixed pitch helicopter is adjusted by bending the blade holders. Two adjustable wrenches work well.

around on the screw. This will make it seem as if the length of a control rod is constantly changing, so check each connection carefully.

TRIM SETTINGS

If the helicopter drifts to the front, back, left, or right, you need to adjust the neutral point of the cyclic controls. First trim the helicopter the best you can with the trims on the transmitter. Next, adjust the pushrod(s) at the appropriate servo shorter or longer as needed, until you have the control in the same position but the transmitter trim at neutral. When you are finished, the swashplate should be very close to being level at neutral.

If the helicopter rotates in a stationary hover, adjust the tail rotor neutral. You can change the pushrod length in a similar manner to the cyclic controls. (See chapter 5 for more details.)

CONTROL SENSITIVITY

If the aileron, elevator, or rudder controls seem too sensitive, you can adjust them for less travel by moving the pushrod connection at the appropriate servo in closer to the center of the servo arm. The pushrod will then move a shorter distance when you move the transmitter stick, and the helicopter response will be reduced.

If the control response is not as great as you want, you might increase the travel of the pushrods by locating them further out on the servo arm. If you decide to do this, check for binding at full travel on each control that is changed. The controls can only move so far before they will hit something at full travel. Test the cyclic controls with collective pitch at both low and high, if so equipped.

On the cyclic controls, aileron and elevator, the flybar weights can have an effect on the control response. Moving the weights out toward the paddles reduces the amount of control available to the pilot, while improving the stability to some extent. By moving the weights in toward the center, the pilot claims more of the control but loses some stability.

You can adjust the sensitivity of the tail rotor or rudder control in one of several ways. First, as discussed, you can move the pushrod connection in or out on the servo arm.

The tail rotor control is also affected by the gyro sensitivity setting. Turning down the gyro sensitivity allows the pilot more control of the tail rotor, making the helicopter rotate or turn, faster for any given stick position. However, with the gyro turned down, the tail drifts around easier. Of course, wind has a greater effect on the helicopter.

If the tail of the helicopter wanders around slowly but constantly, try increasing the sensitivity of the gyro. If you have the sensitivity turned all the way up, increase the gyro effectiveness further by using a longer arm on the tail rotor (rudder) servo. This should only be necessary if the arm is much shorter than recommended.

If the tail of the helicopter swings back and forth quickly and rhythmically, then the gyro sensitivity is turned up too high. Under these conditions, the gyro overreacts to tail movements. As it overshoots the desired position, the gyro calls for opposite control. In extreme cases, this condition continues without stopping.

BALANCE

If your helicopter has a tendency to bobble up and down in forward flight, you might need to add some weight to its nose to hold the helicopter in a nose-low attitude, without having to use as much forward cyclic trim. Another symptom is if a slight back cyclic control input becomes exaggerated to a strong, nose-up movement, most likely when entering or exiting a loop or stall turn.

To check the balance, pick up your helicopter by the flybar. The blades should be facing front to back. The helicopter should hang with the nose slightly low—around two degrees should be a good starting point. If your helicopter exhibits any of the symptoms, try adding one or two ounces of lead to the nose of the helicopter. Secure it to the radio tray, as far front as possible.

HOVERING ROTOR SPEED

Rotor speed during a hover is controlled by the main rotor pitch in both fixed pitch and collective machines. Adjust a collective pitch helicopter by turning ball links, either at the rotor head or at the collective pitch servo. Adjust a fixed pitch rotor head by bending the blade holders of both blades an equal amount.

Reducing the pitch of both blades causes the helicopter to produce less thrust. Since the helicopter won't lift off until sufficient thrust is produced, continue to add throttle until the helicopter does lift off at a higher rotor speed than before. Similarly, by adding pitch to the blades, the rotor speed required to hover will be lower.

The hovering speed of a collective pitch helicopter is also affected by how far the throttle opens as the transmitter stick is moved towards the point where liftoff occurs. By increasing the throttle opening at half stick, you create more lift, allowing the helicopter to lift off without moving the stick quite as far. At this new, lower hovering point, both the throttle and pitch will not be as great. The throttle will be the same as before, but the pitch will be less, resulting in a higher rotor speed. By changing the throttle, you change both the position of the stick and the rotor speed during a hover. By changing the throttle, pitch, or both, you can control the stick position, the rotor speed, or both.

If the rotor speed is too low and the helicopter hovers above half stick, increase the throttle opening at the hover position. If the rotor speed is too low but the helicopter hovers at the proper stick position, increase the hovering throttle and decrease the hovering pitch. If the rotor speed is too low and the helicopter hovers below half stick, decrease the hovering pitch to solve the problem.

If the rotor speed is correct but the helicopter hovers above half stick, increase the hovering throttle and the hovering pitch. If the rotor speed is correct but the helicopter hovers below half stick, you will have to decrease both the hovering throttle and hovering pitch.

If the rotor speed is too high and the heli hovers above half stick, increasing the hovering pitch will solve the problem. If the rotor speed is too high but stick position is correct, decrease hovering throttle and increase hovering pitch. Finally, if the rotor speed is too high and the helicopter hovers below half stick, you will have to decrease the hovering throttle.

With a fixed pitch helicopter, this interaction between pitch and throttle does not occur. The pitch does not change with stick position, so the rotor speed during a hover is not affected by changing the throttle position. Instead, the stick position where the helicopter hovers will be changed, and the actual throttle barrel opening remains the same.

If the stick position is above the halfway point during a hover, lower it by increasing the throttle opening at half stick. If the stick position is below half stick, raise it by reducing the throttle opening at half stick.

With a fixed pitch helicopter, there is nothing else to adjust. A collective pitch model, especially if it is equipped with a helicopter radio, has several other features that can be adjusted to solve problems.

If the helicopter will not drop quickly enough on a landing approach, it might need more negative pitch. If the helicopter drops too quickly when the throttle stick is pulled back fully, reduce the amount of negative pitch.

If the rotor speed increases during a landing approach, use less throttle on the high idle mixing knob. If the rotor speed drops off during a landing approach, more throttle is required on the high idle setting.

The idle mixture on the carburetor can also have an effect on rotor speed during a landing approach. Leaning out the idle mixture increases the rotor speed, and richening it decreases the rotor speed during a descent. To decide whether to change the high idle or the mixture, pay attention to the throttle response as the throttle is increased at the bottom of the descent. If the response is sluggish, the mixture might be too rich; if the response is smooth, change the high idle. If the engine surges during the landing approach and possibly misses slightly when the throttle is increased, then the idle mixture is too lean.

If the rotor speed decreases at full throttle, compared to hover, then either the high speed needle valve is set wrong, or there is too much collective pitch at full throttle. To decide which, observe the amount of smoke that comes out of the muffler. It should remain constant in forward flight as the throttle stick is moved from half to full. If there is more smoke at full throttle, try leaning the mixture slightly. Move the needle valve only one to three clicks at a time, and test again. If there is an improvement, continue until you are satisfied with the results.

If there is less smoke at full throttle than at half stick, try opening the needle valve to richen the mixture. You will have found the best setting for the needle valve when the engine runs consistently at all throttle positions.

If the rotor speed still slows down at full throttle, reduce collective pitch. Having too much pitch places a larger load on the engine than it can handle. The pitch should be reduced in a way that does not affect the pitch setting at hover or low throttle. If your radio has a high pitch trim, use it to make this adjustment. Otherwise, use the differential movement in the collective servo pushrod connection.

If the rotor speed increases at high throttle, you need more collective pitch to place an appropriate load on the engine. A slight increase in rotor speed may be desirable at full throttle, as long as it is not too much. Again, this should be adjusted either by using the high pitch trim on the transmitter or by reducing the differential used at the collective servo.

TAIL ROTOR MIXING

If the helicopter does not rotate during a hover but tries to turn at other throttle positions, then the tail rotor mixing must be adjusted—called *revolution mixing* on most radios, or *tail rotor compensation*.

If the nose of the helicopter rotates to the left as full throttle is applied, then more compensation is required. Turn the up mixing knob toward a higher setting. If the nose of the helicopter turns toward the right at full throttle, reduce the mixing. Turn the up mixing knob to a lower setting.

If the nose of the helicopter turns toward the left when the throttle is reduced below hover, decrease the down mixing. You can observe this most easily during a landing approach. If the nose moves to the right when the throttle is reduced below half stick, increase the compensation. Turn the down mixing knob to a higher setting.

If you are not successful in adjusting the mixing circuit, make sure it is working in the correct direction. Some radios have a switch to set the direction; others allow the adjustment knobs to control the direction, with zero mix in the middle of its range of movement. One or two radios on the market do not offer a way to change the mixing direction. These assume a standard setup with a clockwise rotor head.

To check the mixing direction, adjust the tail rotor pitch to maintain a stationary hover. This will call for 10 to 15 degrees of pitch in the tail rotor blades. Make sure it is in the right direction; if it is not, the helicopter will spin quickly in a direction opposite that of the main rotors.

Start out with the throttle stick at the half position. Make sure the mixing knobs are adjusted higher than zero so some mixing will be evident. Slowly increase the throttle stick, and observe the movement of the tail rotor blades. As the throttle is increased, the tail rotor blades should increase in pitch to compensate for the increased pitch in the main blades. As the throttle is reduced, the tail rotor pitch should move toward zero pitch. At low throttle, the tail rotor blades should have little or no angle of attack.

MECHANICAL PROBLEMS

Careful assembly of your model will help keep mechanical problems to a minimum. Properly balancing and aligning all moving parts will reduce vibration, which is the biggest cause of mechanical problems. If the mechanics do not run smoothly, you can expect to have problems with screws coming loose, ball links wearing out prematurely, fuel foaming, and possibly cracks developing in the frame.

A low frequency vibration often shows itself by causing the tailboom to vibrate up and down, seen most clearly at the very end of the tailboom. The cause is usually found in the rotor head balance—either the blade balance, the flybar balance, or possibly both. If you have already followed the steps for proper balancing during construction, it is time for some trial-and-error troubleshooting.

Take a strip of vinyl blade-covering material or electrical tape and wrap it around the middle of one of the rotor blades (at this point it doesn't matter which one). Hover the helicopter briefly and decide whether there is more or less vibration. If there is an improvement, you have found the blade that needs added weight.

Next move the tape in or out along the length of the blade to find the point of least vibration. If there is more vibration with the tape on this blade, try moving it to the other blade and test again.

If you get the least vibration with the tape all the way at the root of the blade, either your piece of tape is too large or there is no need to add weight to the blade. If you find an improvement with the tape all the way at the tip of a blade, you might still need more weight.

When you have obtained the least vibration possible by moving tape around on the blades, it is time to go on to the flybar balance. To find out which side of the flybar might benefit from extra weight, hang a rubber band over one side of the flybar (the flybar paddle should stop it from coming off). Hover the helicopter briefly and observe the relative smoothness. If there is an improvement, again, you have found the side that needs weight. If there is more vibration than before, move the rubber band to the other side of the flybar and try again.

If you have more vibration with the rubber band on either side of the flybar than you do without, the flybar is already balanced correctly. If you are able to make an improvement by hanging a rubber band on the flybar, you need a permanent solution. If your helicopter has flybar weights, simply move them in or out to adjust the balance. If not, add small collars to the flybar, or wrap tape around the flybar paddle on the side that needs more weight.

If you decide to use tape, experiment with the size of the tape until you obtain the smoothest running helicopter you can. Using the flybar weights, move the weight out on the side that benefited from having the rubber band on it. If both weights are already out all the way, then move the opposite weight in slightly for the same result. Continue to move the weight in or out until you get the best results. If the weights on your helicopter are fairly large, make the adjustments $1/16''$ to $1/8''$ at a time.

The tail rotor can also cause vibration but, because of its smaller size, it is often less severe. If you checked the balance during assembly, you don't need to check it again. If you haven't, remove the entire tail rotor hub and put on a balancer, making sure the blades are straight out. If the tail rotor hub is hard to remove, you can balance just the tail blades.

If the main rotor blade tracking is not adjusted correctly, the helicopter might appear to wobble in every direction, similar to a vibration. In addition, control response will suffer. Correct this by adjusting the high or low blade to run in track with the other.

A high-frequency vibration often shows itself in the form of fuel foaming. More serious symptoms include cracks in the frames and premature wear of parts. The most likely causes center around the engine, but what the exact problem is depends on the design of the helicopter.

If the starting system uses a long start shaft, check the centering of the fan, clutch, and start shaft with a dial indicator. You should find less than .002 inch runout at all locations for satisfactory performance.

If the start cone mounts directly to the end of the clutch or engine, check it for smooth operation. With the engine idling, you should not be able to see any wobble in the starting cone. This can be a problem when the cone is mounted to the end of a plastic fan because occasionally the plastic warps after it is removed from the mold—in which case, you might want to try a new part.

If you still have not found the problem, a last resort is to put all moving parts on a balancer—the fan, clutch, flywheel, start cone, etc. If you find any obvious imbalance correct it by drilling a small hole in the heavy side or by replacing the part.

Proper lubrication will extend the life of your helicopter. Moving parts should be lubricated with oil once per flying session. Open bearings, including gearboxes, should be packed with grease after several flying sessions. If you hear an unusual noise coming from the mechanics, make sure you have lubricated everything. A little bit of oil goes a long way, but don't miss anything.

A high-pitched whine can mean that a bearing needs lubrication. It can also mean that the bearing is slipping on the shaft that it supports. A drop of oil might reduce the noise temporarily, but the permanent cure is to find the loose bearing and secure it to the shaft with thread-locking compound. Remove all traces of oil first. Such a problem is most likely to develop on high-speed bearing applications such as the start shaft, tail drive shaft, and tail rotor gearbox.

A lower pitched, whining noise can be caused by the gear mesh being set too tight on the main gear. Check the clearance with a piece of paper. You should be able to run it through the gears without jamming them. If you feel they are too tight, loosen the setting slightly. This type of problem will show up on the first flight after assembly or repairs, not develop at a later date.

RADIO PROBLEMS

The most common radio problem is what is called a *glitch*, when one or more servos move without the pilot giving a control input. Naturally, such a problem is easily confused with unwanted movements caused by gusty wind or even a pilot error. A radio glitch usually lasts only for a split second, then things will return to normal.

Some radios are more prone to glitching than others. AM radios are more likely to have problems than FM radios. PCM radios eliminate the glitching problem with features called hold and fail-safe. Glitching is caused by the radio responding to an incorrect signal or noise, and a PCM radio ignores these bad signals, holding instead the last good signal. If a good signal is not received for a certain period of time, fail-safe takes the servos to a predetermined location, usually low on the throttle and neutral on all other controls. Therefore, a glitch on a PCM radio is a sudden loss of control called a *lockout*, not an unexpected movement.

Any number of things can cause glitches. For example, strong radio signals near your flying site can overpower your radio. (This is more of a problem in some areas of the country than others.) Changing to a different channel might be the only answer if such problems persist. Try to get more information from other local flyers or a nearby hobby shop to confirm whether the channel you are using has a reputation for having problems in your area.

A more common cause of glitching can be found on your helicopter itself. Metal-to-metal contact can cause occasional radio interference and usually affects AM radios more than FM ones. Check for loose bolts on your helicopter wherever two pieces of metal are fastened together. The main frame is a good place to look if your model has aluminum frames. The landing skid-to-strut connection, if it's all metal, is another possible place.

Bearings naturally have metal-to-metal contact that can't be avoided. If you hear any chattering or whining coming from a bearing, it could lead to radio problems. Lubricate the bearing, or replace it if necessary.

If a glitch only affects one channel and always the same one, the problem could be in the servo. A dirty or worn control pot in the servo can give erratic control response. You might be able to observe this by slowly moving the servo with the transmitter stick. If the servo pauses while you are still moving the stick, there may be a bad spot on the pot. The servo might also jump ahead to a new position. Repeat the test several times to confirm the problem. Finally, to eliminate the chance that the problem is in the transmitter, plug in a different servo to the same channel in the receiver. Slowly cycle the servo and observe its movement. If the response is smooth now, you have confirmed that the servo is at fault. The manufacturer can usually service a bad servo, or you can replace it with a new one.

The location of the receiver antenna can affect a helicopter's potential for glitches. By moving the antenna, you might be able to put it where it won't pick up noise from the mechanics as easily. A whip antenna works best because it is short and can be placed at the front of the radio tray, away from the mechanics of the helicopter (FIG. 7-2).

7-2 A base-loaded whip antenna is more convenient than the full-length wire antenna supplied with the radio. In addition, the use of a whip antenna can reduce glitches by allowing you to keep the antenna away from the helicopter mechanics.

Charge your batteries fully before each flying session. Transmitter batteries will last for around two hours of use, which should be adequate for a day of flying, as long as the radio is turned off whenever possible. If you spend a lot of time working on the radio adjustments between flights, check the transmitter battery condition before flying again.

Your transmitter should have a meter that shows battery condition. If it is a signal-strength meter, the antenna must be raised fully for it to work. Do not touch the antenna while checking the meter. If your meter is a voltage meter, turn on the transmitter and check the reading. With either type, watch for a sudden drop from the normal reading. Usually a red zone on the meter indicates when it is unsafe to fly, and you should abide by it to avoid loss of control. If you are flying with a group of modelers, make sure your channel is clear before turning on the transmitter to check its meter.

The flying time available per charge is determined by the equipment on the helicopter. The size of the battery will have the greatest effect. The use of a gyro will reduce the flight time available, so you should use a larger battery pack when you use a gyro.

As the voltage decreases in the flight pack battery, servo response will slow down. The gyro motor will slow down, making it less effective. When you notice these symptoms while flying, land immediately. You might have only a minute or two of battery life remaining. To avoid this danger, use a battery meter to check the condition of the batteries. If you like to put in many flights in a day, check the voltage before each flight. When the voltage drops below 4.8 volts, it is time to recharge the batteries.

NiCad batteries, as found in both the transmitter and receiver packs, can fail with prolonged use. If you use them properly, they're good for 1000 charge/discharge cycles. On the other hand, allowing the batteries to fully discharge (by leaving the system turned on) can shorten the life of the batteries.

Because the battery packs are made up of four or eight cells, you might not notice that one cell has gone bad. A greatly reduced charge life is a sign that there might be a bad cell in the pack. The fully charged voltage will be lower than normal. To play it safe, replace the entire pack with a new one.

If the radio does not work after a crash, check for broken wires at all connections. A suspected switch can be bypassed by plugging the battery pack directly into the receiver. If you can't find an obvious problem, send the radio out for repair. Follow the directions included with the radio for where to send it to be serviced, and be sure to explain the problem fully to the service technician.

Chapter **8**

Product
reviews

Now that you have a working knowledge of
how RC helicopters are put together, how they fly, what can possibly go
wrong with them, and what you can do to fix it, it's time to move on to
specific models. This chapter provides an overview of ten different products including both radios and kits. The chapter explains their advantages
and disadvantages, their extras and their idiosyncrasies. My advice is
based on my own experience with these brands, so you should feel free
to experiment to find what works best for you.

AIRTRONICS VANGUARD RADIO

The Airtronics Vanguard FM 6H is an excellent radio choice for the first-
time helicopter pilot. It has all the essential heli features with nothing
missing, but it doesn't have any extra "bells and whistles" on the radio
that a beginner would find more confusing than helpful.

Transmitter

The transmitter case on this radio is constructed of black plastic, with a
satin chrome finish on most parts that gives an attractive appearance (FIG.
8-1). The controls are laid out in the familiar Mode II locations, with throttle and rudder on the left, and aileron and elevator on the right. (Mode I is
also available.) The control stick lengths and centering spring tensions are
adjustable. Electronic trims for the four primary channels are located ad-
jacent to the control sticks.

A trimmer panel is located on the front of the transmitter below a
hinged cover. Figure 8-2 shows the trimmers available on this radio: revolution mixing, dual rates, throttle hold, high pitch trim, idle-up, and servo reversing. Inhibit switches are provided for the revolution mixing and throttle hold
functions.

There are five toggle switches on the transmitter. On the upper front

8-1 The Airtronics Vanguard 6H FM helicopter radio provides the features most important to beginners. Also, switches on the transmitter are easy to reach during flight.

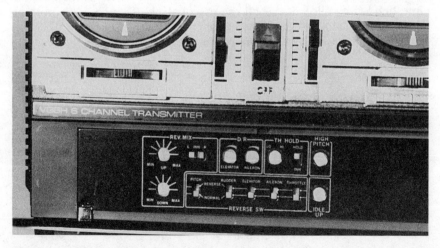

8-2 A hinged front panel provides access to the mixing adjustments and servo reversing switches. The location on the front of the transmitter is convenient for making adjustments at the flying field.

edge, a switch above each control stick is used to control the dual rate functions. The aileron dual rate switch is on the right, and elevator is on the left. When the switch is pushed up, the dual rate function is turned on, reducing the servo throw in accordance with the setting of the appropriate dual rate trimmer.

A pair of toggle switches are located on the top left corner of the transmitter. The one closest to the pilot controls the throttle hold function. When this function is engaged by pushing the switch to the back, the throttle servo goes to the spot determined by the setting of the throttle hold trimmer. The throttle stick now controls only the collective pitch servo. With the throttle hold position set to a low idle, the pilot can practice autorotation landings without having to restart the engine each time.

When the throttle hold switch is engaged, the collective pitch range is expanded on the top end by taking the high pitch trimmer out of the circuit during an auto. The collective pitch servo can then use its full throw on the top end rather than the reduced amount set by the high pitch trim. You can easily adjust the radio to 8 degrees of pitch for forward flight and 10 to 12 degrees for an auto.

Behind the throttle hold switch is a taller one which controls channel 5. You can use this for retracts, lights, etc., but the most common use for this channel is to select the sensitivity of a dual-sensitivity gyro.

On the top right corner of the transmitter is a switch to control the idle-up function. With this function engaged, the throttle servo will not go below a predetermined point. Use idle-up to maintain rotor rpm when the throttle stick is pulled back to the low-pitch range. For example, during a landing approach the throttle stick may be pulled back all the way to allow the helicopter to descend. Without idle-up, the throttle would drop to an idle. Without the engine, rotor speed would drop off, making the controls sluggish.

On the upper front panel of the transmitter, you'll find a knob near the center that is used to adjust the pitch trim. It works the same way as the primary control trims, adjusting the neutral point of the collective pitch servo. You will probably use this knob to control the pitch at hover. Because the pitch trim offsets the entire range of pitch servo movement, it will have an equal effect on high and low pitch settings.

The Airtronics Vanguard transmitter is powered by a 9.6-volt 600-mA NiCad battery pack that goes behind the door on the back of the transmitter. The battery has a plug on the lead so you can change packs if necessary. If you bump the transmitter when setting it down, make sure the battery hatch is closed securely. You might want to add a more secure catch, considering the consequences of having the battery pack fall out while flying.

Receiver

A model 92765 receiver is included with the Vanguard FM system. It is a Dual Conversion, 7-channel FM narrow-band receiver, measuring $2^3/4'' \times 1^3/8'' \times 7/8''$. The receiver is claimed to provide outstanding range, noise suppression, and adjacent-channel rejection. A PCM version is also available to accompany the Vanguard PCM 6H radio.

Servos

Four 94102 standard servos are included with the radio system. They are rated at 50 oz./in. of torque, which should be suitable for most applications. However, to take full advantage of this system, you need to purchase a fifth servo. If you do not already have a gyro, Airtronics offers a package that includes both the gyro and a specially equipped servo, and buying them together will save you money.

Better still, Airtronics has a high-power ball-bearing servo available that is packaged in the same size case as their standard servo. This is the 94738 servo, which is rated at 75 oz./in. of torque. This would be the perfect servo to use on collective pitch, due to its high power and increased durability.

Extras

All the usuals are included with the Airtronics Vanguard—rechargeable flight battery pack, charger, switch harness, servo mounting hardware, etc. (FIG. 8-3). The battery pack is the standard 500-mA size, but this is

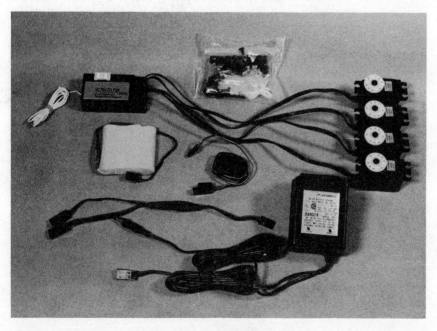

8-3 Complete flight pack and accessories, as supplied with the radio. The receiver is a dual-conversion narrow-band design. Four servos are supplied, and the battery charger has a separate LED for the transmitter and receiver packs as well as very long leads for convenience.

barely adequate for helicopter use when a gyro is powered by the same pack as the rest of the system. A 1000- to 1200-mA pack is more suitable.

The battery charger provided is a wall unit, with long cords to reach the transmitter and airborne charge receptacles. A separate LED monitors the charge status of each circuit. This is much nicer than a single LED that changes colors when the transmitter, receiver, or both packs are on charge. A 50-mA charge rate is used for both the transmitter and receiver packs, giving a standard charge time of 12 to 16 hours.

Flight testing

I put my new Vanguard FM 6H radio in a Shuttle ZX helicopter to try it out. The standard-size servos fit easily, with room to spare in the servo openings. To complete the system, I added an Airtronics 96252 gyro. (This is their better gyro, with dual sensitivity controls, switchable in flight.) I also substituted a 1000-mA battery pack to extend flight times between charges.

The transmitter is comfortable to hold, with all switches easily reached while flying. I especially like that engaging the throttle hold switch provides additional positive pitch at full stick—which helps during the last moments of an autorotation landing, increasing the amount of lift available as rotor speed bleeds off. The Airtronics Vanguard is the first beginner's radio I have seen with this feature. To take advantage of it, adjust the collective pitch servo linkage for the maximum amount of positive pitch you want. Then, use the high pitch trimmer to reduce the positive pitch to an appropriate amount for forward flight.

FUTABA 5NLH RADIO

Futaba has a complete line of helicopter radios to suit any pilot. The Futaba 5NLH Helicopter Radio System consists of a transmitter, receiver, four servos, battery pack, switch harness, and charger. It is intended to be an entry-level radio, so it includes all the necessities for flying an RC helicopter. It also has a few "bells and whistles."

Transmitter

The heart of the 5NLH system is the transmitter. The case is a comfortable design based on the original Conquest series, which is similar to the current Attack 4 aircraft radio (FIG. 8-4). The control sticks are of the open gimbal design, with adjustments for both stick length and spring tension.

Electronic trims are provided for the four flight controls. The throttle trim is of the ATL type (Adjustable Throttle Limiter). It provides full trim control at idle, but has no effect on the servo position at full throttle. A bracket on the front of the transmitter is provided for attaching the included neck strap.

The 9.6-volt NiCad battery pack is behind the rear cover. With the cover removed, you can see the switches that control the servo-reversing

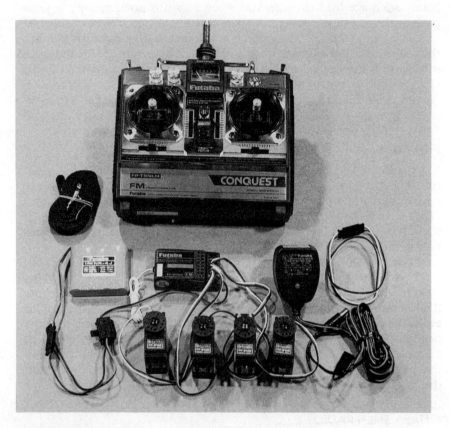

8-4 The Futaba 5NLH radio control system is designed for beginners. The most essential helicopter features are found on the transmitter. A dual conversion, narrow band receiver and four servos are supplied, along with a 500-mA battery pack and charger.

function for each channel. All other adjustments are located externally on the transmitter.

A row of three knobs and a control pot are located across the top front edge of the transmitter. The pair of knobs on the left control the revolution mixing circuit. The left knob of the pair is labeled up mix; the right one is down mix. Turning either of these knobs clockwise will increase the amount of revolution mixing for the respective portion of the throttle stick movement.

Above the right control stick is a knob that is labeled pitch trim. It adjusts the pitch servo in the same way as any of the primary flight trims adjust their channels. The pitch trim allows the pilot to offset the servo up to 15 percent of full throw in either direction, for a total change of 30 percent. You use it to achieve the proper collective pitch setting when you are trimming out a helicopter.

One drawback with this type of pitch trim is that it affects the full range of pitch travel, from low to hover to high. Solving a problem with one setting might actually create a problem somewhere else. For this reason, try to use the pitch trim only for minor adjustments or for experimenting with different settings. Make major changes at the servo arm/pushrod connection.

The last control on the right of the row is labeled throttle rate, and it is used to adjust the position the throttle servo goes to when the throttle hold switch is engaged. (The throttle hold switch is located on the top right side of the case, where it can be easily reached during flight to practice autorotation landings.) When you pull the switch toward you, the throttle servo goes to the predetermined position, usually a low idle, while the throttle stick continues to provide full control of collective pitch. When the switch is pushed to the rear, normal operation of the throttle resumes.

On the top left side of the transmitter is a switch for the idle up function. Pulling this switch toward you engages idle up, which is used to keep a constant rotor speed during low collective pitch portions of flight, such as steep descents during landings and aerobatics that involve brief periods of inverted flight.

When idle up is engaged, the throttle servo will never go below a preset position, usually somewhere near quarter-throttle. This is similar to the action of the idle trim, but with an expanded range. Using the full amount of idle up stops the throttle servo from moving below the half stick position—which is fine for rolls, but causes too high of a rotor speed during a landing. If you choose the idle up function for aerobatics, switch it off for landings. Instead, advance the throttle trim to maintain rotor speed during landing approaches.

The idle up adjustment is located on the rear of the transmitter. Turning the pot to the left increases the minimum throttle position when idle up is turned on; turning the knob to the right disables the idle up feature. Always make sure to turn off the idle up before starting the engine, or you could damage the clutch from the unexpectedly high idle speed.

Also located on the rear of the transmitter are a pair of trimmers labeled aileron and elevator AST, or Adjustable Servo Throw. These adjustments allow you to choose how sensitive the aileron and elevator controls are, similar to adjusting the low-rate setting on a radio equipped with dual rates. Turning the control pot fully clockwise gives maximum control throw, while turning it counterclockwise reduces the total servo movement on each side of neutral by as much as 60 percent, which is useful if you're a beginning helicopter pilot who overcontrols your helicopter. Then, when you are ready for a more responsive machine, a simple adjustment at the transmitter provides it.

Receiver

The transmitter might be the most important part of the radio to the pilot, but when it comes to dependability you need a good receiver. The receiver included with the Futaba 5NLH is the R128DF 8-channel narrow-band dual-conversion FM receiver. The addition of a dual conversion design featuring an ultra-narrow-band ceramic filter should make for a very solid radio link. **Note:** This receiver is the same one provided with the most expensive Futaba FM systems.

The R128DF receiver measures 2.5″ × 1.4″ × 0.8″ and weighs 1.6 ounces. The current drain is rated at 26 milliamps, and the expected range is in excess of ¼ mile on the ground and ½ mile in the air. As usual, visibility of the model is the actual range limiting factor.

Servos

Futaba includes four of their S-148 servos with the 5NLH radio. The S-148 is the latest in the 128-138-148 series, which has always been the most common servo size, and is more reliable than ever with the use of surface-mount technology and a new, direct-wiring system that eliminates all wiring inside the servo case except for the connector lead. The motor and control pot are soldered directly to the circuit board, eliminating the risk of a wire breaking due to vibration. The rated output torque for this servo is 42 oz./in. with a 60-degree transit time of 0.22 seconds. The case measures .77″ × 1.59″ × 1.58″, with a weight of 1.5 oz. While this should be more than adequate for any of the small to mid-size helicopters on the market today, Futaba has recently introduced the S9201 servo, especially designed for the rigors of helicopter flight.

Extras

To get the full benefit of the features on this radio, you need to buy a fifth servo to use on collective pitch. Also, you'll probably find the addition of a gyro useful in controlling the tail rotor.

Futaba has three gyro models available for use with their radios. I chose the G154 model to use with this radio in a Kyosho Concept 30. The G154 is the lowest priced gyro available from Futaba and also the most compact. It receives its power from the shared flight pack battery, drawing 160 mA of current. The 500-mA pack included with the system provides power to the receiver, the five servos, and a gyro for approximately one hour, so you should use a larger capacity battery pack, such as a 1200-mA size.

Also available are the G152 and G153BB models. The features of both models are similar, but the 153 has a ball bearing added to the pivot inside the gyro. Both models have provisions for using a six-volt independent power supply with voltage regulation. Also, two sensitivity adjustments are provided, and you can select the one you want to use with the retract switch on the transmitter, which is much like a dual-rate control. Both features are nice to have, but I would still recommend the more basic G154 for any beginner, especially with the smaller helicopters.

Checking it out

I installed the radio equipment in a new Concept 30 DX to try it out. When I hooked up the collective pitch pushrod, I found it necessary to use some differential in the servo arm by offsetting the pushrod connec-

tion about 25 degrees forward (toward high pitch) from the neutral position. A high pitch trim adjustment on the transmitter would have accomplished the same thing more easily, but I was able to get the desired
pitch settings at all throttle positions with this adjustment.

I adjusted the up and down mixing knobs next. With my installation, I
got the best result with the up knob set at five and the down knob set at ten.

The Futaba 5NLH radio is one of the least complicated helicopter
radios available. If you want to keep expenses to a minimum, while still
having the most important helicopter features, this radio is worth considering. If you would like more features, one of the other radios in the
Futaba line is likely to offer what you want.

GMP REBEL

Gorham Model Products simplified helicopter design many years ago
when they developed the Cricket. As a basic .25-powered helicopter, it
was the vehicle chosen by many modelers when they first ventured into
the world of RC helicopters. GMP went on to design and produce many
larger, more sophisticated models. As the state of the art has continued to
advance, the trend has been toward higher performance, more complicated models. This trend has carried over into trainers, as well as sport
and competition models.

The GMP Rebel uses a fixed pitch Hiller control system for simplicity.
A .40 to .45 size engine provides the power, and you don't need a special
helicopter engine with this model (FIG. 8-5). The Rebel uses a new rotor

8-5 The GMP Rebel is a fixed pitch helicopter that can provide a relatively inexpensive
introduction to helicopter flight. The rotor head and control system is simple to
adjust, and a standard aircraft radio is suitable for flying the Rebel.

head design consisting of a one-piece nylon center unit supported by dual ball bearings on the hub. This design has a lower parts count than any other rotor head on the market because the flexibility of the nylon takes place of several moving parts, thereby further improving the durability and simplicity.

The kit

The Rebel might be basic in design, but the parts in the kit are of very high quality (FIG. 8-6). Many of the parts are made of aluminum, anodized black for a nicer appearance, while others are made of steel or nylon where suitable.

8-6 These are the parts that make up the GMP Rebel kit. A one-piece metal frame is used for strength. The canopy is vacuum-formed of clear plastic.

The parts are packaged in bags, labeled in the order they will be used, and they correspond to the steps in the instructions. All the fasteners are in bag 1, and the remainder of the bags hold the parts needed for each major assembly of the helicopter. I still like to see the fasteners divided up and packaged with the assemblies they will be used on, but that's obviously a lot of extra work for the manufacturers, so I'm not surprised they haven't done it this way.

Construction

Assembly starts with preparing the engine for installation by mounting the fan, clutch, and starting cone. When choosing an engine, GMP recommends using a ball-bearing-equipped engine in the .40 to .50 size range because of the sideways load applied by the toothed drive belt. Also for this reason, you shouldn't overtighten the drive belt.

The cooling fan cover is vacuum-formed of clear plastic. It is made in two pieces and must be trimmed and glued. I would have preferred a molded fan cover that bolts together to eliminate a lot of the trial-and-error fitting; you have to trim this fan cover until it fits over the end of the fan.

The main frame consists of thick aluminum of one piece, rather than two thin pieces. While in this type of construction, the bearings and bell-cranks are out in the open, with the more typical two-piece frame, most of the parts are trapped in the middle. The one-piece frame doesn't look as nice, but it is much easier to assemble and maintain.

The landing gear consists of aluminum skids and struts joined by metal strips wrapped around the skids. The instructions mention the possibility of using small screws to secure the skids in place, and I highly recommend you do so. The skids seemed tight enough on my helicopter, so I left the screws out, but after the first flight, one of the skids had turned halfway around.

The servo trays are made of die-cut plywood parts that must be glued together, then bolted to the frame. Round off the front corners of the top tray to protect the canopy from possible damage, and paint the wood first to protect it from fuel and oil. A spray can of flat black paint works well—the flat finish hides the wood grain better than gloss, and it matches the black anodized surface of the aluminum quite well.

Assembly of the rotor head revolves around the plastic centerpiece. It is supported on the metal hub by two ball bearings. The bolt that passes through the bearings is a bit difficult to tighten because the nut is recessed inside the plastic centerpiece. I added a washer to the bolt before putting the nut on, and spaced it out slightly to tighten it with a wrench. You could also use needle-nose pliers to reach inside the plastic recess. Either way, make sure the bolt is tight enough or the center unit will wobble on the hub.

The instructions state that the tail rotor drive wire is cut to the proper length. However, GMP has had problems in the past with some of the wires being too short, so they are now shipping them at least 1/4 inch longer than necessary. When measuring, make sure all setscrews are removed that could stop the wire from fully seating. A Dremel cut-off wheel works best for cutting wire to length.

The same clamps used to mount the tailboom to the frame are also used to mount the tail fins. Use the oversized washers here to protect the wood parts. Horizontal and vertical stabilizers should be painted first—for a shortcut, try using Monokote. The vertical fin is made of a Magnalite product, an unusual material consisting of end-grain balsa sandwiched between layers of fiberglass cloth. It is very light but still strong.

The canopy is vacuum-formed of clear plastic. The two halves must be trimmed to an even width on the flanges. You can put a narrow lip on the back edge to help strengthen the canopy. Use inserts to provide a track for the canopy to slide on over the lower servo tray (FIG. 8-7). You

8-7 The completed radio installation on the Rebel. Note where the front corners of the upper servo tray have been beveled to protect the plastic canopy. Radio installation is simple on the Rebel, with straight pushrods between the servos and bell-cranks.

can trim and glue them in place before you join the canopy halves. Glue a scrap piece of plastic to the inside of the canopy over the seam at the top and bottom so it won't come apart when the back edge is stretched open while sliding over the canopy mounts.

The kit supplies a Sullivan 8 oz. tank which is held onto the tank support with rubber bands. It might be a good idea to mount the tank with servo tape first, then secure it with the rubber bands just in case, to stop it from sliding around on the mount.

The instructions recommend high-quality servos to improve performance and reliability, but this is true for all helicopters. With the GMP Rebel, any full-size servo should be adequate. Mount the servos with the screws and grommets supplied with the radio system. I normally like to wrap the receiver and battery pack in foam, then secure it with rubber bands around the radio tray. However, this is not practical on the Rebel because the sides of the tray must be clear to slide into the tracks of the canopy. Instead, I used servo mounting tape to hold the receiver, battery, gyro, and its control box in place.

Full size drawings are supplied showing the pushrod lengths. There are only five rods used on this helicopter, so adjustment should be easy. Aileron and elevator rods must be cut to length. The drawing shows a

Z-bend connecting each rod to its servo. I don't especially like Z-bends, but it is a convenient way to make the connection. Ball links or solder links could be substituted if you wish.

Flying

The Rebel is aimed at modelers that might already have some equipment from fixed-wing flight, so I used an O.S. Max 40FSR engine that I had in a Quickie-500 plane. I also used the radio from the airplane, a Futaba eight-channel J-series, although only four channels are used on the Rebel.

The engine location makes starting a breeze. The glow plug is easily accessible from the side, and the cone starter is located between the rear landing struts. A helicopter starter extension for the electric starter makes it easier to reach the cone. If you don't have one at first, you can use the full-size starter. Just turn the rubber insert around so the small hole faces out. You might have to tilt the starter slightly to avoid hitting the landing strut, but it will work.

My test model experienced a vibration problem at hover speed. Although the normal balancing procedures would not help, the problem was easily cured. By adding more pitch to the main blades, the rotor speed was lowered below the point where the vibration started. I found that $6^1/2$ degrees of pitch worked best. The blade holders as supplied in the kit provided only 5 degrees. Incidentally, this problem arose because of a change in airfoil on the rotor blades. The new blade has more drag, which makes it easier to slow the rotor head down to descend. A side effect is that the new blade also provides less lift at the original angle of attack. The new instruction manual will list the higher pitch setting. The die used to form the blade holders is also being changed, so if you get a new kit there should be no need to change the pitch angle.

With a fixed-pitch helicopter, you have to anticipate when a throttle change is necessary. When you pull back the throttle to drop a little bit, you must get back on the power right away or the helicopter will continue to drop while you wait for the rotor to speed up. By using a light-weight rotor head and blades, GMP has reduced this problem as much as possible.

A pilot making the transition from fixed wing to helicopter flight might not notice the lag in control response that is inherent in a fixed pitch design. A side benefit is that when the throttle is reduced suddenly, the helicopter does not fall out of the air as quickly as a collective pitch machine does. Because for most people it's a natural reaction to chop the throttle when they get into trouble, the slower rate of descent might be beneficial. The three other controls—aileron, elevator, and rudder—have a nice amount of control authority.

Since this helicopter has only Hiller steering, I was surprised by how well the cyclic (aileron and elevator) controls worked. The only time it was obvious that I was flying a fixed-pitch machine was when it was time to land. When you reduce the throttle to descend, the blades slow down. Unfortunately, the control response slows down with the blades. I found the best way to land the Rebel was by making a circling approach, with each circle a little bit lower, so I did not have to reduce the power much below half stick.

The Rebel is an excellent choice to test the water with, so to speak. It provides an inexpensive introduction to helicopter flight using a design that is easy to build, adjust, and maintain. The simple control system allows you to spend more time learning to fly and less time learning to adjust your helicopter. Being able to use a radio and engine that you might already own is a further benefit.

When this book was written, it appeared that the GMP company had gone out of business. Rebel kits might be available for some time, and Tech Specialties handles repair parts. In addition, it is possible that the design will be "kitted" by another company in the future.

HIROBO SHUTTLE

The Hirobo line of helicopters is distributed in the United States by Altech Marketing. Hirobo started the trend toward .30 size helicopters several years ago when they introduced the Shuttle, the first .30 size helicopter to offer performance similar to that of larger machines. As an added bonus, the Shuttle was shipped with all major assembly completed at the factory, and probably this feature alone was most responsible for the tremendous response from the modeling community. The popularity of helicopters continues to grow today because of the ease with which a novice pilot can obtain a flight-worthy model.

Since the Shuttle was first introduced, there have been three major versions available. The rotor head design is the most important change in each, but there are other differences as well. The first model is no longer available. It featured a smaller version of the Hirobo DDF (Dual-Damp-ened Flapping) rotor head. While this rotor head offered smooth stable flight, it was very prone to tailboom strikes caused by the rotor blades being able to droop too easily during a hard landing.

The original Shuttle was eventually replaced by a newer version that used a one-piece blade axle shaft to support the blade holders. O-rings at each end provide dampening. This model is still available, and can be ordered in a special Shuttle XX version, which has ball bearings installed instead of bushings at all major wear points.

The newest version to come along is the Shuttle Z (FIG. 8-8). The Z model has longer rotor blades and a longer tailboom than the base model. The tail rotor uses the sliding collar pitch change design. Most impor-tantly, the Shuttle Z uses the new Hirobo FZ rotor head, which breaks Hirobo tradition by switching to the popular underslung flybar design, offering a more compact rotor head and shorter pushrods. The FZ rotor head also uses a one-piece cross axle to support the blade holders. This limits the flapping movement of the rotor blades to an absolute minimum. The rotor blades, besides being longer, are also weighted to improve auto-

8-8 The Hirobo Shuttle ZX, shown here, has many high-performance parts to suit both the experienced helicopter pilot and the beginner. Less sophisticated models are also available.

rotation ability. If you manage to get a boom strike with this helicopter, you earned it!

Altech/Hirobo offers a fully tricked-out Shuttle named the Shuttle ZX. It has 18 extra ball bearings besides what is standard on the Z model, and it also has a tailboom brace. These parts are available separately, so you can upgrade a Z to a ZX model.

The kit

The Shuttle ZX comes packaged in a two-piece, molded styrofoam container with a cardboard sleeve over it. The styrofoam is shaped on the inside to hold all the components of the kit securely during shipping. With this packaging, there should be little chance of receiving a damaged model.

The main part of the mechanics consists of the side frames, which house the drive gear and support the rotor head and tailboom. As you take it out of the box, you will see that all the work has been completed on the mechanics. With the prebuilt version, an Enya .35 engine is installed at the factory. Even the muffler and fuel lines are already in place. The rotor head is installed on the main shaft, and all control linkages are in place.

The tail rotor assembly consists of the gearbox, blade holders, and pitch change mechanism. (In this case, "gearbox" might not be the right word because the Shuttle uses a toothed belt to drive the tail rotor.) The "gearbox" houses two ball bearings that support the tail rotor shaft, with a drive pulley located between the bearings. The pitch change mechanism consists of a bellcrank controlling the position of a yoke that slides on the outside of the tail rotor shaft (FIG. 8-9). All of these parts are already

8-9 The tail rotor assembly on the ZX uses a collar that slides on the outside of the tail rotor shaft to change the tail rotor pitch, offering very smooth, precise tail rotor control.

installed onto the end of the tailboom. The drive belt, too, is in place, with a piece of cardboard holding the belt tight at the open end of the tailboom.

The remaining parts in the kit are the landing gear and the main rotor blades. You can easily assemble the landing gear by following the instructions. While the landing gear is constructed of plastic struts and aluminum skids, the rotor blades are made of wood, with lead weight installed at the factory to improve performance. The blades are already covered with heat shrink tubing, and the blade root reinforcements are in place. In other words, just bolt them on and fly (FIG. 8-10).

Assembly

Now that you have the box opened and the kit spread out over the workbench, it's time to get started putting it together. Of course, you have a big head start with the prebuilt kit. It may not be "ready to fly," as the package claims, but at least ninety percent of the work is finished already.

8-10 Major components of the Shuttle ZX ARF kit, ready for final assembly. The majority of the work has already been done at the factory. (A standard kit is also available.)

Start by mounting the tailboom. The drive belt passes through the boom, and must have a 90-degree twist in it to line up with the drive pulley. The instructions clearly show which way to twist the pulley, but if you are not sure if there is more than a quarter turn on the pulley, let the tailboom hang by the belt to untwist it. The belt has teeth on it to match up with the pulleys, so you shouldn't have a problem with slippage unless the belt is extremely loose, in which case, adjust it by sliding the tailboom in or out.

The landing gear consists of two nylon struts and two aluminum skids. The Japanese version of the Shuttle ZX has an all-aluminum landing gear, but this has been changed in the U.S. version to suit our taste for nylon struts. I believe the nylon version is a better choice because it absorbs the shock of bad landings much better.

The landing gear is held onto the frame of the helicopter by four self-tapping screws. I wouldn't be surprised if one or more of these screws strips out of the plastic eventually. If that does happen, you can easily substitute a 3 mm bolt and locknut.

While you don't have to install the engine, I will briefly mention it. For the U.S. market, Altech/Hirobo has installed an Enya Super Sport 35 Heli engine. This engine features a heat-sink head and TN style carburetor. It has two ball bearings on the crankshaft and a ringed aluminum piston. The TN carburetor uses the familiar twin-needle design, with the idle mixture needle located on throttle arm side. To accommodate the

Enya engine, Altech/Hirobo makes a special fan hub for the Shuttle that has the necessary slot to fit the crankshaft key used on Enya engines.

Radio installation

I chose an Airtronics Vanguard FM 6H radio to test out the Shuttle. The Vanguard is available as a six-channel heli radio, in either RM or PCM versions, and the most important features for heli flight are found on this radio: throttle to collective pitch mixing, high pitch trim, tail rotor compensation, idle up, and throttle hold. Servo reversing and dual rates are also found on the radio.

The Shuttle is designed to accept all popular servos. An extra set of holes are provided in the servo tray to fit either large or small servos. You can use either four or five servos, but for best performance I suggest you use a helicopter radio with five servos. The instructions show the proper installation methods for either four or five servos. **Note:** Be careful to follow the correct diagrams as you proceed with the installation.

A separate drawing explains how to hook up the pushrods to each servo arm. The distance from center to pushrod connection on each arm is specified, with an optional, larger amount shown in red for aerobatic performance. You'll also notice that some of the servos call for the neutral point to be located ten or more degrees off-center. This is done in some cases because the pushrods feed off the servo at an angle, in other cases to provide a different amount of travel on each side of center. While this information is shown clearly in the drawings, it is not explained well in the text.

The collective pitch range is specified as +6.5 to −1.5 degrees, with 5.5 to 6.0 for a hover. After flight testing, I found the low and hovering pitch suggestions to be correct. However, the Enya .35 was able to handle considerably more top end pitch than suggested. I found +8.5 degrees to work well at full throttle. Using less pitch will not allow you to take full advantage of the power available.

Directly in front of the fan shroud is a space to house the gyro. Use double-sided tape to both mount and isolate the gyro sensor. A space molded into the frame to hold the switch harness is a very convenient location for the switch, since there is no need to remove the canopy to get at it. The wires for both the gyro and switch harness can be fed through the frame and over the fuel tank to get to the servo tray area (FIG. 8-11).

Flying

The Shuttle ZX flies very smoothly at any speed. It is very stable in a hover, yet responsive when you want it to be—for example, you can easily perform tight loops.

The collective pitch offers precise control at all times, which is especially obvious at the end of a landing approach. Just a slight movement of the control stick is all it takes to stop the descent. Tail rotor control is equally effective.

8-11 The completed radio installation on the Hirobo Shuttle ZX. An Airtronics Vanguard radio is shown.

The Shuttle ZX has what it takes to do a nice autorotation. The blades are weighted to increase the inertia in the rotor head to give a little extra time at the end of an auto, allowing for a soft touchdown. In addition, the longer length of the rotor blades increases the disk area, providing the same effect as lowering the wing loading on a fixed wing craft. This is one .30 size heli that can auto with the best of them.

JR MAX 6 RADIO

The JR line of radios is distributed in the United States by Hobby Dynamics Distributors. Among the radios produced by JR are several models specifically for model helicopter use, ranging from basic five-channel units to sophisticated 10-channel models that can store the settings for several helicopters in memory (FIG. 8-12).

The Max computer radio is a beginners model that offers the most important features of more complicated radios through the use of a computerized control system. All adjustments to the transmitter are made through a menu that is displayed on a small LCD screen on the front of the transmitter, and four buttons move through the menu and to change settings.

A six-channel transmitter is supplied with the Max computer radio. The case is made of black plastic, with chrome trim on the front. A carrying

8-12 The JR MAX 6 computer radio is a beginner to intermediate system. Adjustments are made through the computer program, using the buttons on the front of the transmitter.

handle on the top of the transmitter also doubles as a support for setting the transmitter on the workbench or ground. Ergonomic styling—including rounded finger grips and a textured surface to prevent slippage—makes the transmitter more comfortable to hold.

Switches on the transmitter control various functions during flight. The retract switch, on the left, controls channel 5 and can also be used to operate extra functions, such as retracts. More commonly, though, you'll use it to control gyro sensitivity with switchable gyros.

Dual rate switches are used to vary the control sensitivity of the aileron and elevator channels (cyclic). They are located on opposite corners of transmitters, with elevator on the left and aileron on the right. Either switch position can be used for low rate, depending on how you choose to adjust the radio.

Inboard of the dual rate switches, a knob to the left of center is used to control the pitch trim. Its use affects the entire range of pitch servo movement. To the right of center, a long-handled switch controls the idle up circuit. With this switch engaged, rotor rpm can be maintained while the throttle stick is in the low pitch area. When the idle up switch is engaged, a separate low pitch setting also takes effect, giving you the flexibility to adjust the helicopter for various flight stages, such as hovering and aerobatics.

On the top right corner of the transmitter is the throttle hold switch, used to perform autorotation landings by holding the throttle servo at idle while the pitch control continues to function. The throttle servo position is adjustable through the computer control system.

Features found on most radios, such as servo reversing, are normally controlled by small switches or trimmers. With a computer radio like the MAX, all features are adjusted by use of the menu system. Pressing the up and down cursor keys simultaneously will allow the transmitter to enter Function Mode. From here, you can move through the menu of available options, changing settings as needed. These include the usual servo reversing, travel adjust, and dual rates. Helicopter specific functions include throttle curve, pitch curve, throttle hold, and revolution mixing.

All settings are expressed as a percentage of full travel, with 0% being neutral, and + or − 82% being full travel left or right (up or down). You can increase or decrease these settings as necessary. In addition if you decide to start over with the factory-default settings, you can use the reset function provided.

The throttle and pitch curves are adjustable at three points—low, hover, and high. These are abbreviated on the display panel as A, C, and E, but you don't have to memorize them because the front panel of the transmitter lists the abbreviations for each function.

Receiver

The JR Max Computer radio system is equipped with an NER-627X seven-channel receiver—a PCM design that provides increased reliability. A single conversion design is used in the receiver to reduce size and expense, while ABC & W technology is incorporated to minimize possible interference. The receiver measures 2 inches long by $1^3/8$ inches wide by $7/8$ inch thick, and weighs 1.8 ounces. All servo plugs fit into a block on one end of the case, making it easier to wrap the receiver in foam before installing it in the helicopter. As an added bonus, the amplifier for the JR gyro systems is the same dimensions as the receiver in top view, making it simple to wrap the two items together.

Servos

The radio system is supplied with five NES-L501 servos. The torque on these servos should be adequate for most applications, especially for small to mid-sized helicopters. For more demanding applications, you might want to upgrade to a more powerful, ball-bearing-equipped servo.

Battery

A 1000-mA battery pack is included with the helicopter radio system, eliminating the need to upgrade to a larger battery pack when adding a gyroscopic stabilizer. Also, the radio includes a suitable charger to match the transmitter and receiver battery packs.

KALT ENFORCER

The Kalt line of helicopters is produced in Japan and includes a full range of sizes, with designs to suit everyone from the beginner through the competition-oriented pilot. Of particular interest is the Kalt Enforcer kit, which is a new design that is gaining popularity.

The Kalt Enforcer is distributed in the United States by Hobby Dynamics Distributors. It is a .30 size helicopter, available as either an ARF or standard kit. The design of this helicopter breaks new ground in several areas, particularly in its modular construction and its use of planetary gearing in the drive system.

Kit assembly

When you look at an assembled Enforcer, the modular construction is not evident (FIG. 8-13). Once you start building the kit, however, you'll begin

8-13 The Kalt Enforcer is shown with a JR X-347 radio. A Webra Speed .28 ABC engine and Kalt muffler are installed in the Enforcer shown. This helicopter sports many features desirable to beginners, while offering flight performance to suit advanced pilots.

to understand what "modular" means. The mechanics of the Kalt Enforcer are assembled in several sections, and each module is comprised of one or more sections (FIG. 8-14).

The main mechanics of the helicopter consist of the main frame, the transmission, and the engine section. The tail section is made up of the tailboom, the tail rotor, and the gearbox. The main rotor head is assembled as a separate unit. The radio tray is assembled and joined to the front of the main unit.

8-14 All major components of the Kalt Enforcer have been assembled into modules. The remaining steps will put it all together. If you buy the ARF, this is close to how it would look as received.

The Enforcer kit comes with all its parts separated by assembly step and sealed in plastic bags. The bags are labeled to match the number of the assembly step, making it very easy to find all the proper parts while putting the kit together. Better still, a small bag numbered for each assembly step contains all the fasteners—screws, nuts, and washers—saving a lot of time and confusion picking through one large bag of fasteners for each step.

The instructions are divided into two parts. The ARF instructions are first, followed by the standard kit instructions. If you are building a standard kit, you have to go to the middle of the book to start assembly. When you finish the last step of the instructions, you will have a helicopter that is similar to an ARF kit. At this point, turn back to the beginning of the book and follow through the ARF instructions for joining the largest modules and installing the radio system.

The instructions are easy to follow because they are broken down into many small steps. The drawings that accompany each step make it easier to visualize what you must do. In addition, the instructions include comments that clarify difficult steps. The instruction book is published in the United States by Hobby Dynamics Distributors, and this is probably why the instructions are so good, since they are not just a literal translation from Japanese to English.

As you start assembling your kit, the modular design will become more and more evident. As you complete each major assembly step, you can put aside the previous module until you reach the final stages. Only a few screws hold each section together, so repairs should be easy with this design approach.

Kit construction starts with the landing gear and main frame. The landing gear struts are molded of nylon, like the rest of the frame. The struts are made in left and right halves with self-tapping screws joining each side of the frame. The screws go into a nylon cross brace between each side of the frame. **Note:** Make sure you use 3-×-18 mm screws to join these pieces, instead of 3-×-10 mm as called for in the instructions. (Both screws are supplied in the kit.) Even the longer screws have been known to strip out, so be careful not to overtighten them.

Your assembly continues with the planetary gearing and transmission. While the planetary gearing is one of the more unusual features of the design, you can't even see it once the helicopter is assembled. The gearing runs very smoothly, with practically no drag. The pictures in the instruction show the gearing design much better than I could explain it.

Install the swashplate and related control system parts next. An unusual feature in this area is the collective pitch control mechanism. A pushrod passes through the hollow main shaft. At the bottom, it is connected by a ball bearing to the pitch arm. At the top, two joiner rods are connected to the pitch rod, going down from the top and connecting to the mixing base. As the mixing base moves up and down, the collective pitch of the blades changes accordingly.

This method of pitch control seems to be a very clean system. The benefits include not having to deal with a swashplate that slides up and down and being able to locate the pitch control servo connection away from the rest of the controls. When you look at a picture of the finished radio installation, you will see that the pushrods are all in a straight line. The pitch control design helped to make that possible (FIG. 8-15).

Before assembling the control system parts, I recommend that you polish the plastic balls with 600-grit sandpaper. Some of the balls in my kit had a very slight amount of molding flash on them, which can wear out the nylon ball links quickly if you don't attend to them.

Next comes the motor preparation and installation. Remove the prop driver washer from the engine first. Special clutch spacer sleeves are supplied with the kit to fit Webra, OS, and Enya engines; choose the appropriate one and place it on the shaft.

At this point, I suggest checking to make sure that the threads on the engine crankshaft go all the way down to the top of the clutch spacer. On the Webra 28 that I installed, the crankshaft threads stopped about 2 mm short of the spacer, a condition that won't allow the fan hub to tighten against the spacer as it should. If you run into this problem, drill out the back of the fan hub to clear the unthreaded portion of the shaft. In the case of the Webra, I used 1/4" drill bit to drill out the threads to a depth of 2 mm, which still left more than 75% of the threads intact.

Put on the steel prop nut supplied with the engine after you place the fan hub, to prevent the hub from coming loose. (Hobby Dynamics intends to have Webra thread the crankshaft further on their engines in the future. If they do, you will not have to drill out the fan hub as I did.)

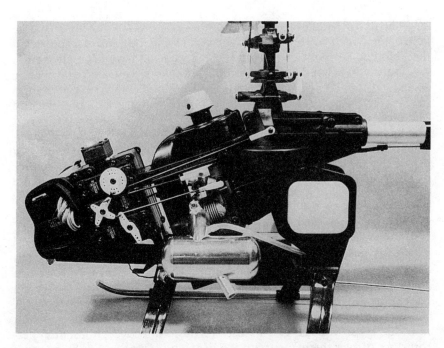

8-15 The completed radio installation on the Kalt Enforcer. A JR X-347 radio is shown. All pushrod runs are in a straight line from the servo to the control bellcrank, showing a well thought-out design.

A two-piece molded fan shroud wraps around the engine, directing cooling air over the engine cylinder. The only trimming you need to do is around the exhaust port, to make room for mounting the muffler.

Assemble and mount the servo tray next. Slide plates are used to compensate for different size servos. A platform is molded into the trays to hold the receiver and battery pack.

Next comes the tail rotor assembly. The tail blade holders are fastened to the hub with two ball bearings on each side. Pitch change is via a sliding collar, which seems to be standard practice on most helicopter designs now.

The tail rotor gearbox is driven by a steel wire inside the tailboom. Each end of the wire has a loop formed in it, which fits into a slot molded into the tail input gear shaft at the back and a similar shaft at the front. This should prove to be a fool-proof system because there are no set-screws to come loose.

Start off the main rotor assembly by joining the blade holders to the spindles. Each blade holder pivots on two ball bearings. The spindles are fastened to flapping yokes made of spring steel—another of the unusual design features. Rather than using some form of rubber dampening in the rotor head, this model has a steel plate or yoke on each side that supports the blade holders while allowing them to flex up and down. If the yokes ever become bent in a crash, you can change them easily by removing only three screws on each side.

The flybar paddles included with the kit are very long for a .30 size helicopter, which was obviously done to increase the control response on the Enforcer. From my own flight tests, it seems to have been effective.

Once you reach this point in the instructions, your Enforcer will be assembled to a degree similar to the ARF version. Plug the tailboom in next—a simple procedure, since the tail drive wire has a loop in the end that plugs into the tail drive shaft.

Radio installation is also simple on the Enforcer. The servo tray is adjustable to fit different size servos. The gyro sensor is mounted to a plastic tray located below the main shaft, with a clear plastic cover to protect it from fuel and oil. The gyro amplifier goes up front with the receiver and battery pack. A platform at the front of the servo tray holds these parts, with rubber bands securing them in place.

The servo-to-bellcrank pushrods all run in a straight line on the Enforcer. When you set the neutral point on the servos, keep in mind that the servos are angled down at the front (the diagrams in the instruction book show this clearly). The pushrods should meet their respective bellcranks at a 90-degree angle. Because the pushrod is slanted down, the bellcrank will be slanted back at the neutral point. The top edge of the bellcranks are level.

You have to finish the rotor blades supplied in the kit. Slots are cut near the tips so you can glue in lead weight to improve autorotation performance. Cover the blades with the heat-shrink tubing, but be warned: the material supplied in my kit was a bit harder to work with than what I am used to. It was heavier than usual and harder to shrink. If you have trouble with the covering, consider replacing it with a different brand of blade covering.

Now for the cosmetics. The canopy and fins are formed of a tough flexible plastic. A tinted windshield goes on the front of the canopy, but you have to trim the edges first.

I found an easy way to mark where to trim the edges. First, secure the windshield in place with masking tape. Next, put strips of masking tape around all the edges to show where to cut. Remove the windshield and trim it with scissors. Finally, put the windshield back in place with a few strips of tape, then fasten with the screws that are supplied. Add some self-adhesive decals, and the Enforcer is all dressed up and ready to go.

The canopy fastens in place in a very clever manner. Two clips molded into the frame catch the bottom edge. After they are engaged, plastic snaps at the back fit into holes drilled in the canopy.

Flying

To test the Kalt Enforcer, I installed a JR X-347 radio system, a computerized radio capable of flying airplanes, gliders, or helicopters. To complete the system, I added a JR 120 gyro stabilizer system, which is a very compact gyro featuring ball bearings on the sensor motor. It also has two sensitivity settings, selectable in flight.

The top cone start makes it easy to get the Enforcer's engine running.

There are no special adaptors needed, just the standard one supplied with the starter, which is especially nice for the modeler making the transition from fixed wing to helicopter flight; he or she can use the same starter for both type of aircraft.

The Enforcer was easy to trim out. The only thing I had to change was the collective pitch range. The instruction book suggests 7 degrees for hovering, and 10 degrees for top-end pitch. From previous experience, I felt this would be too much, so I started out with a little bit less. By the time I was done with adjustments, I settled on 3^1/$_2$ degrees of pitch for hovering, and 7^1/$_2$ degrees at full throttle. On the low side, -2 gives a nice landing approach. For autorotations, -4 on the bottom and $+10$ on the top works well. These settings only apply to the blades supplied with the kit. Other blades that I tried required higher pitch settings which were more in line with those suggested in the instructions. The JR X-347 makes it easy to get these different settings.

The Kalt Enforcer is suitable for both the novice and the experienced pilot. It hovers well, yet is capable of any aerobatic maneuver imaginable. The mechanical design has proven to be reliable. Also the Enforcer should be an easy helicopter to maintain due to its modular construction.

KYOSHO CONCEPT 30

The Kyosho company has been involved in several phases of radio control modeling for many years. They recently branched out into the helicopter market with the release of the Concept 30 design. The Kyosho line is produced in Japan but it is available in the United States through Great Planes Distributers.

The Kyosho Concept 30 is produced in three levels of trim. There is a DX model for beginners, an SE model for beginners through advanced pilots, and an SX version for those wanting top performance. While the SE and SX models are available only as traditional kits, the DX can be purchased either as a kit or preassembled. The assembled version is even available with an O.S. 28 FH engine already installed.

The DX model has been designed to offer the beginner as much stability as possible by using metal flybar paddles instead of the traditional plastic ones. The heavier metal paddles slow down the control responses, while improving stability (FIG. 8-16).

While the DX model has ball bearings at all vital wear points, the SE model has additional ball bearings taking the place of some bushings, improving the smoothness and durability of the helicopter. The collective pitch slider is of a slightly better design on the SE.

The SX model has the same improvements found on the SE model, but the SX has been upgraded to better handle the demands of aerobatic flight. The plastic balls in the control system are replaced with metal ones for added smoothness and durability. The collective pitch travel range is increased to allow extended inverted flight. Finally, a sleeker canopy separates the SX from other Concepts.

8-16 The Kyosho Concept 30 DX is an ideal beginner's helicopter. SE and SX models are also available, offering higher levels of performance and quality.

Kit assembly

The Concept 30 is constructed of a variety of materials, the most common material being plastic. Where extra strength is needed, though, aluminum or steel has been used. The wise choice of materials yields a model that is easy to construct and durable in a crash (FIG. 8-17).

The Concept 30 instruction book is easy to follow. Assembly is broken down into 35 steps, with a separate drawing for each. Each fastener needed for a step is shown in a box on the left side of the drawing, making it easier to match up the parts before starting a new step. The instructions are so complete there is no need to explain each step here. Instead, I'll just go over the highlights.

Construction begins with the rotor head assembly. I started by checking the fit of the ball links on the molded plastic balls. The molding flash that was present on most of the balls stopped the links from moving freely, so I used some 600-grit sandpaper to remove the flashing. Once everything worked smoothly, I proceeded with the assembly.

One of the see-saw bushings was a tight fit on my kit, while the other was fine. The problem seemed to be in the plastic, so again I sanded the plastic until the bushing fit properly. When checking the fit, twisting the brass bushing left a mark on the plastic that made it easy to see where to sand off more plastic. This should not be a problem on the SE model, since the brass bushings are replaced by ball bearings.

Be sure that the screw holding the flybar in place is tight enough. Once the top cover is on the rotor head, you won't be able to check the

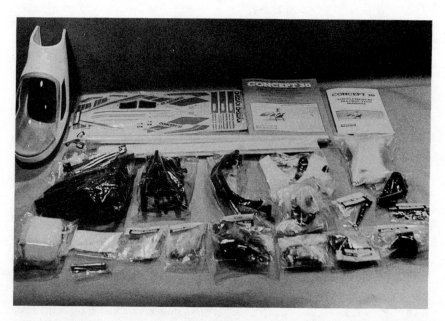

8-17 The parts that make up a Concept 30 are divided up into packages by component, such as side frames or landing gear. The Concept 30 DX is also available as an ARF model, with or without the engine installed.

screw again. You might want to drill a small hole in the top of the rotor head cover to allow access to this screw. It will make subsequent adjustment and replacement of the flybar much easier (FIG. 8-18).

Once the rotor head assembly is completed, add the pushrods. The instructions show a full-size view of each pushrod, making it easy to adjust the ball links to the proper initial settings. The instructions point out that the ball links are one-sided, meaning they will only fit over the balls one way. The Kyosho logo must be visible to the outside of each installed link. This type of design is intended to make a more secure ball link fit, but it has the disadvantage of not allowing half-turn adjustments during flight trimming.

After assembling the rotor head and preparing the main frames, put together the radio tray. This is one of the nicest parts of the kit because the radio tray is molded of plastic and assembles easily in five minutes or less. If you have ever looked at a helicopter kit with a wood servo tray, you will appreciate how much nicer the plastic one is. One note here: Although the instructions don't call for the servo and gyro installation until step 23, you might find it easier to install the equipment before the tray is attached to the rest of the helicopter.

It's obvious Kyosho built the Concept around an O.S. Max engine. The fan shroud was a perfect fit around the carburetor and heat sink head of the O.S. 32 engine that I used. If you choose another brand of engine, it should be no problem to cut out the plastic fan shroud as needed to fit.

8-18 On the Concept 30, you might want to drill a small hole in the center of the rotor head top cover. This allows a 1.5 mm allen wrench, shown, to reach the flybar-retaining set screw without removing the top cover.

Once the engine and fan shroud is in place, you can join the main frames together and mount the radio tray and fuel tank. Don't forget to put the fuel tank in place before sliding on the radio tray: the tank is captured by the radio tray and can't be installed later. At this point you might notice that the gearing feels tight. As long as it doesn't feel extremely tight, don't worry about it. After one or two flights everything should loosen up—at least, this has been the case with every Concept 30 that I have seen.

The tail rotor gearbox and tail rotor assembly are next. Be sure to use thread-locking compound where suggested in this crucial area. Also, please note that the gearbox assembles over the tailboom. If you put together the gearbox first, the alignment pins won't allow it to fit all the way onto the tailboom.

The instructions show the proper servo installations for either four or five servos. Again, to get the full benefits of a helicopter radio, you need to purchase an extra servo, which will allow independent control of the throttle and pitch servos. Otherwise, follow the four-servo installation drawings. The servo tray is designed to accept all popular servos, with slots for the mounting screws providing some flexibility in dimensions. Plastic plates are provided for the mounting screws, holding the servos in place.

Now we get to the most complicated part of any collective pitch helicopter radio installation, the throttle and pitch pushrod connections. In the instruction book, step 26 applies to four-servo installations, and steps 27 and 28 are for five-servo setups. If you are using a helicopter radio that

does not have a high pitch adjustment, such as the Futaba 5NLH that I used, I would suggest that you follow step 26 for installing the collective pitch servo arm and pushrod. The drawing in step 26 shows the amount of differential movement r
properly. Step 28 shows th
will only work properly w
used to reduce the amoun
shows the throttle pushrod

The body mounts qu
bracket at the front and tw
the back. Pressure-sensitive
cut out, they can be placed

Once you mount the rotor blades you make final adjustments to the collective pitch control. Use one blade to check all settings, then adjust the outer blade to match. This will give you a head start on getting the blades in track on the first flight. As a final check, make sure all the controls move in the correct direction. The instructions show each transmitter control stick movement and the corresponding helicopter movements, which should prove helpful to the novice helicopter pilot.

As I mentioned earlier, the kit that I am reviewing is the DX version. I chose a Futaba 5NLH radio with S-148 servos to control my Concept. A Futaba G-154 gyro completed the radio installation. Power is provided by an O.S. Max .32 helicopter engine, which has proven to be an excellent combination.

Flying

If you follow the instructions, you will be rewarded with an excellent helicopter for learning this challenging hobby. For advanced pilots, a little extra control throw on each channel will provide the perfect helicopter for trying new maneuvers and for just plain burning holes in the sky. Although a .60 size machine might fly better, it can also be a bit intimidating. I have seen many experienced heli fliers take a step back from their .60 size machines to try a Concept 30. Invariably, because they are less afraid of crashing, they are more willing to try harder maneuvers, thereby increasing their skills.

To see how the Concept 30 would work as a trainer, I set mine up according to the instructions. With a set of training gear installed, I turned over the controls to a friend who had never flown a heli before. I briefed him on the basics of flight, warning him never to get over 6 inches off the ground. By the end of the first tankful of fuel, he was able to steer the helicopter wherever he wanted. Thankfully, he followed my advice of staying very close to the ground, and was able to go 10 to 15 seconds at a time without having to cut the power and land. With a reasonable amount of self control, it should be possible to learn to hover the Concept 30 in a fairly short time with little or no damage to the helicopter. The key is going one step at a time, without jumping ahead beyond your abilities. After all, you can't learn how to fly if your helicopter is on the workbench waiting to be fixed.

MFA SPORT 500

The MFA Sport 500 is kitted in England by Model Flight Accessories and imported by Hobby Lobby International. The Sport 500 is MFA's first venture into the helicopter market and, as such, it is intended to be an introductory model. The Sport 500 uses a .40 to .45 size engine, making it one of the larger trainers. The control system is of fixed-pitch design for simplicity, using a Hiller type teeter rotor for directional control (FIG. 8-19).

As expected, this type of helicopter is fairly simple to adjust, but the simplicity comes at the expense of sluggish vertical control and soft cyclic control. This does not mean the helicopter cannot be flown successfully, merely that the controls are not as precise as more complicated collective-pitch Bell and Hiller machines.

If you wish to upgrade your Sport 500 kit, both collective pitch and autorotation kits are available separately. Finally, a Scale Hughes 500 fiberglass fuselage can be purchased to enclose the Sport 500 mechanics.

Besides the Sport 500 kit, you will need a strong .40 to .45 size engine, at least a four-channel radio, and preferably a gyro. You'll need a minimum of special tools—mainly just a saw to cut out the wood parts for the radio tray. (A jigsaw would come in handy for this work.)

Most of the screws supplied with this kit are of straight slot, pan-head type. Also, most of the nuts are plain, not locknuts, probably to keep costs down. For this reason, it is important to use a thread-locking compound with practically every bolt. Otherwise, you will surely have re-

8-19 The MFA Sport 500 is a fixed pitch helicopter designed to be an inexpensive introduction to helicopter flight.

peated troubles with parts coming loose in flight. Changing the bolts and nuts to a better grade could be too expensive, but you might want to consider just changing over to locknuts, still using the bolts as supplied.

The construction part of the instruction book is divided into 31 steps. Setup and flying are covered in separate sections. Pictures of vital steps are included, but they are all at the end of the booklet, rather than next to each step.

Construction

Assembly of the Sport 500 kit starts with the main frame. The frame is one piece of aluminum, with flanges bent on the front and back edges. Mount the landing gear (also aluminum) to the frame first.

Next, assemble the clutch. Mount the clutch shoes with springs to the large pulley. Refer to the pictures often while doing this, and please note that the bolts that pass through the clutch shoes must not be tightened fully. Once these bolts are fastened to the pulley, they will form the pivot point for the clutch shoes. If the nuts that hold the shoes in place are too tight, the shoes will not be able to move easily. You will have to glue the clutch lining in place in the clutch bell. The instructions do not say what kind of glue to use, so I tried CyA glue, with satisfactory results.

Make sure the bearing blocks that support the idler shaft are oriented correctly, as explained in the instructions. A small cotter pin is used to hold the clutch bell to the shaft. At first glance, this does not seem appropriate on a helicopter but in practice, it has proven to be adequate. In fact it provided a shear bolt effect, protecting the mechanics from more expensive damage if the rotor head would stop suddenly in a crash.

Before installing an engine, secure the flywheel, fan, small-toothed pulley, and starting pulley with the prop nut. All this is a lot of stuff to be mounted all on one shaft, and it proved to be hard to hold securely. Tighten the prop nut as tight as possible, using a socket wrench if you have one.

When mounting the engine to its mounting plate, the 3 mm measurement given is more important than it might appear, because it determines the alignment of the fan shroud with fan. Once joined, the two halves of the fan shroud might have a tendency to hit the fan. If this is the case, try gluing the shroud together with silicone seal. If you must remove it in the future, you can easily separate the two halves with a knife.

The main shaft—or the *mast*, as they call it—is mounted along with the drive gear and bearing blocks. You might have to file off the rough edges from the ends of the shaft before slipping it through the bearings. It's also easier to fasten the large metal gear to the shaft first, slip on the bearing blocks, then mount it as a complete assembly rather than mounting it step by step.

To assemble the tail rotor, join the blade holders over the bearings. It is extremely important here to use thread-locking compound on the screws that hold the bearings to the hub. Also, use stepped washers as a safety measure, in case the bearing fails. The stepped side should face the bearing to allow free movement under normal conditions.

The instructions recommend painting the tail rotor blades and tail fins, but it is much easier to balance the blades if they are covered with heat shrink tubing or self-adhesive covering instead of paint. When you mount the tail blades, I suggest substituting locknuts. Because the bolts must be loose enough to allow the blades to move, you won't be able to tighten the standard nuts securely enough to keep them in place. You can cover the tail fins with iron-on covering to eliminate the need to paint them.

Mount the tail rotor gearbox to the tail fin, suspended below the tail-boom, to leave the drive wire out in the open. Use thread lock generously on the screws that secure the drive wire to the coupling; these screws can come loose easily, causing complete loss of tail rotor control. Adjust the tail drive supports vertically so there is no load on the drive wire either up or down. Oil this area frequently since the metal drive wire is running in a metal hole with no bearing or plastic bushing.

If necessary, sand the swashplate control bellcranks in the bushing area so the pivot does not bind when you tighten the mounting screw. Also, note that the two bellcranks won't be identical when you are finished putting on the brass balls. Take note of which one is which when you are mounting them to the sides of the frame.

While assembling the rotor head, I found that the hole in the mast/ rotor joiner was too small for the stepped pivot. Drilling it out slightly solved the problem. Also, make sure the set screw that secures the teeter wire faces straight up so it will be accessible if you have to replace the tee-ter wire later.

Temporarily install the rotor blades so you can adjust the coning angle. Figure 8-20 shows the side view angle of the blades compared to a line coming straight out from the rotor head. To adjust the coning angle, hold the center plate of the rotor head in one hand and grasp the rotor blade at its root. By pulling up on the rotor blade, you can bend the top and bottom blade mount plates at the same time to give the proper angle. A wooden gauge comes in the kit to measure the coning angle. The aluminum plates are soft, so it is easy to bend to the proper angle.

The radio tray is made of wood. The kit supplies two sheets of ply-wood, with the parts outline printed on them. You must first drill the holes, then cut out the parts on the outline. An electric jigsaw is best for this, but a coping saw will do the job.

A nice feature of the servo tray is that the location of each servo is labeled directly on the wood, along with the correct control direction and proper location for each pushrod (FIG. 8-21). For this reason, I recommend you use clear paint or glue to fuel-proof the wood; it would be a shame to cover up the markings.

Next, install the servos as directed and hook up the controls according to the markings. The tail rotor is a flexible cable running in a plastic

8-20 The Sport 500 uses a fixed pitch rotor head, constructed mostly of aluminum. Bend the blade holders to achieve the proper coning angle and pitch angle.

tube. You have to solder couplers onto the ends of the wire, and you should anchor the plastic tube to the tailboom with plastic ties or electrical tape.

At this time, install the receiver, battery pack, switch, and gyro, then do the canopy work. Cut out the canopy from the plastic sheet and join it. With the Sport 500 kit, the left and right canopy halves are molded in one sheet of plastic, with the rear edge of each being joined together. To separate them, cut the two parts down the middle. While this is a bit harder to do than just trimming the edges as in other kits, the final results are similar.

Once you have trimmed the two parts, glue them together and paint them. When you drill out the two screw holes for mounting, use a larger size drill, then install a rubber grommet that will fit the supplied bolts. You should be able to find suitable rubber grommets at an auto supply store. Adding the grommets helps prevent the bolts from wearing through the plastic—which happened to me.

Before you mount the rotor head, slip the swashplate driver onto the main shaft to keep the upper portion of the swashplate turning with the rotor head. The flybar control rod passed through it. Finally, bolt the rotor head to the main shaft—at this location, I recommend you substitute a locknut for the plain one that is shown on the plans. Don't take any chances at this crucial place.

To wrap up, check the blade pitch on each side of the rotor head. (The kit supplies a plywood gauge.) If you must change the pitch, use two adjustable wrenches: put one on the blade holder plates over the blades and the other on the plates directly over the blade joiner so you don't damage the wooden blades by trying to twist them.

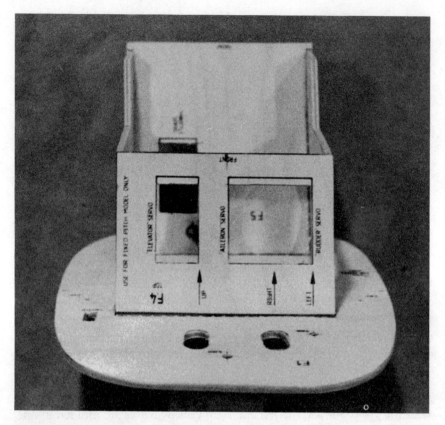

8-21 This is the Sport 500 servo tray after assembly. Note how the servo cutout was modified to fit a smaller size servo. Be sure to check this before cutting the opening.

Flying

The instructions go on to cover briefly the setup and flight training. However, because the Sport 500 is a fixed pitch design, you don't need to do much during setup. Adjusting the needle valve correctly is probably the most important thing to do.

The flight performance of the Sport 500 is adequate for learning. Perhaps the best application for this helicopter, however, is for a modeler who would like to try helicopter flight without investing the amount of time and money required for a full featured helicopter. The Sport 500's design has a high degree of survivability in a crash and, while parts might bend easily, they can also be bent back into shape with little effort.

SCHLUTER JUNIOR 50

Robbe Modelsport in Belle Meade, NJ, imports and distributes the Schluter line of helicopters. In the early 1970s, Dieter Schluter was the first individual to successfully mass-produce a model helicopter in kit form.

Today Robbe Modelsport offers several fine models. For the entry level pilot there is the Junior 50. Also offered are the Magic and the Scout 60, which obviously use .60-size engines.

All three of these helicopters use the same rotor head and control system, referred to as System 88. Like many of the fine RC helicopters being manufactured today, most use high-tech plastic/fiber composites for many rotor head components.

The Schluter Champion has been regarded as the most revolutionary helicopter of its time. It was the first helicopter to feature an underslung flybar, giving the pilot crisper control. Many other models incorporated this feature into their designs with great results.

In the Schulter line, the Junior 50 is most often recommended for learning. It is a nice compromise in many ways—size, price, and quality. The majority of the Junior 50 mechanics are based on various .60-sized helicopters in the Schluter line. The control system and rotor head is the System 88 design, which is also used on the Schluter Scout and Magic (FIG. 8-22).

8-22 The Junior 50 by Schluter is not only good for learning to fly, but is also a good choice for experienced pilots. The helicopter features aluminum side frames, with a steel and composite plastic rotor head.

The kit

Like all Schluter kits, the parts for the Junior 50 are packaged in bags labeled to match the assembly step, and all fasteners are included in the appropriate bag so you can find the right parts when you need them. Besides the usual instruction booklet, four large mechanical drawings are included, showing an exploded view of each section of the helicopter. These plans are sure to come in handy when ordering replacement parts, too, because part numbers are labeled on the drawings.

Assembly

First, prepare and join the aluminum side frames. (A metal channel and spacers hold the two halves in proper alignment, forming the main frame for the helicopter.) Then assemble the landing skids and add them to the main frame next.

The main shaft is supported by ball bearings, which are held in place by molded plastic bearing holders. The holders consist of two halves that wrap around the bearings, and threaded metal tubes that are pressed into holes in the bearing holders. Once you have assembled the tubes to the frame, you'll thread bolts into them to keep the bearing holder in place.

The main shaft slides into the bearings, and is held in the proper location by collars. Flat spots that are gound into the shaft should be under the setscrews before you tighten the screws. (Flat spots allow for easy removal.)

You must assemble the clutch system to the Junior 50 mechanics before installing the motor. The added bonus is that you can easily remove the engine later without disturbing the gear alignment settings. Connect the engine to the clutch with three plastic bushings and pins; the bushings fit into holes in the clutch, and matching pins are located on the end of the fan hub. You'll find that this system works quite well, relieving some of the need for accuracy in the engine, fan, and clutch assembly. For best results, use a dial indicator to check the runout in the fan installation.

The tail rotor drive consists of a wire running through the tailboom, supported at several locations by plastic bushings. The wire is driven by a bevel gear, contacting the rear side of the motor pinion gear. Assemble the tail rotor gearbox next; it consists of two shafts supported by four ball bearings. Bevel gears transfer the power from one shaft to the other, so be sure to put the small and large gears on the proper shafts.

The Junior 50 swashplate is molded of plastic and fitted with a steel pivot ball and a large ball bearing. The control connections are through brass balls held in place with 2 mm screws and nuts. Be sure to use thread-locking compound when fitting the control balls, then add the pushrods connecting the bellcranks to the swashplate. To make adjustments easier, the kit uses spacers on the rods between each ball link.

Next assemble the main rotor head. The blade holders each consist of two shells, which fit over the support shaft bearings. Pay close attention to the instructions and detail drawings to be sure assembly is done correctly. When you're done you should have a very precise, durable rotor head, the same one used on most of the Schluter .60-size machines.

The control mixer allows the three servos (collective pitch, elevator, and aileron) to tilt together. The collective pitch servo movement causes all three servos to tilt, thereby raising or lowering the swashplate. Aileron or elevator movement tilts the swashplate in the appropriate direction. The swashplate movement on the Junior 50 is offset 45 degrees counterclockwise to make pushrod connections easier. The design of the rotor head allows for this offset, giving the intended control input.

Once assembly is completed, radio installation and adjustment follows. The instructions included in the kit cover this well, but one place might cause a misunderstanding. The directions mention pitch range travel of −4 to +9, which is suitable for experienced pilots. However, the instructions also mention +2.5 degrees as a midpoint during adjustments, and you should use this only to check alignment of the servos and bellcranks, not as a hover point. In practice, you will find that +5 degrees works well for hovering.

As this book was going to publication, I learned that a Junior 50 is now available in an ARF model.

Flying

The Schluter Junior 50 is suited to both flight training and aerobatics. You can adjust the control response to suit your needs by varying the servo travel, and also by changing the position of the supplied flybar weights. Two styles of flybar paddles are available, a thin design for extreme aerobatic performance, and thicker hollow paddles for smoother performance.

The control system on the Junior 50 has virtually no slop in it due to the use of metal balls inside the links, and nylon bushings in all bellcranks and mixers (FIG. 8-23). You can easily replace the bushings if they ever show signs of wear—as you can the metal balls and plastic links. This makes it easy to maintain the helicopter in optimum flying condition.

8-23 The Junior 50 uses the System 88 control system. The result of the tilting servo control mixing system is a very precise control system, absent of any free play.

MINIATURE AIRCRAFT USA

In this product-review chapter I would be remiss if I did not mention the Miniature Aircraft models. As you have no doubt noticed throughout this book, Miniature Aircraft's X-Cells are quite common in the RC heli world (FIG. 8-24). The company is owned and operated by the Schoonard family and located in Orlando, Florida.

Miniature Aircraft USA was started by the late Walt Schoonard and is carried on by sons Tim and Ted. Both are serious world-class competition flyers who constantly refine the X-Cell helicopters. When Walt decided to start on his own, he blended all of what he considered to be the best features of the top model helicopter kits available. The results are a fine example of modern technology correctly applied.

All of the X-Cell models feature autorotation clutch, collective pitch and composite rotor heads. The difference between models are the rotor diameter and engine displacement; as the size of the engine increases, the rotor diameter also increases. Regardless of the engine size you choose, you'll find quality parts, convenience, and superior design.

8-24 The X-Cell 30 is the smallest helicopter in Miniature Aircraft USA's X-Cell helicopter line. It shares some key parts with the larger X-Cell helicopters, making a very strong helicopter.

Appendix

Addresses

Airtronics Inc.
11 Autry
Irvine, CA 92718
Phone: 714-830-8769
Airtronics radios

Altech Marketing
P.O. Box 391
Edison, NJ 08818-0391
Phone: 201-248-8738
Fax: 201-248-0970
*Hirobo helicopters, Enya
engines, and other helicopter-
related products*

**Academy of Model
Aeronautics (AMA)**
1810 Samuel Morse Drive
Reston, VA 22090
Phone: 703-435-0750

Bob's R.C. Helicopters
820 Shakespeare Dr.
Beaumont, TX 77706
Phone: 409-866-0973
Helicopter-related products

Bolar Heli Research
322 North 7th St.
Lehighton, PA 18235
Phone: 215-377-4941
Helicopter-related products

Capstone R/C Suppliers, Inc.
562 West Schrock Road
Westerville, OH 43081
Phone: 614-899-6313
Helicopter-related products

Carstens Publications
P.O. Box 700
Newton, NJ 07860
Phone: 201-383-3355
Flying Models Magazine

Dave Brown Products
4560 Layhigh Rd.
Hamilton, OH 45013
Phone: 513-738-1576
RC helicopter simulator

**Don Chapman Design
Corporation**
6225 Taylorsville Road
Dayton, OH 45424
Phone: 513-236-8853
*Whispertech, V-tech, and other
helicopter-related products;
Tuned pipes and mufflers*

Dr. J's
45640 Twenty-Third Street
Lancaster, CA 93536
Phone: 805-949-3586
Helicopter items

Dubro Products, Inc.
480 Bonner Rd.
Wauconda, IL 60084
Phone: 312-526-2136
Helicopter-related accessories

FHS Supply, Inc.
P.O. Box 9
Clover, SC 29710
Phone: 803-222-7488
Red Max fuel

Futaba Corporation of America
555 West Victoria Street
Compton, CA 90220
Phone: 213-537-9610
Futaba Radios, YS engines

Golden Gate Hobbies
P.O. Box 282005
San Francisco, CA 94128
Phone: 415-342-5581
Helicopter-related accessories

Great Planes
P.O. Box 4021
Champaign, IL 61820
Phone: 800-637-7660
Helicopters and related products

Helicopters Unlimited
276 Wood Pond Rd.
Cheshire, CT 06410
Phone: 203-271-2938
Helicopter related products

Heliscene/Heli Images, Ltd.
The Barn House, Cromer Road
Thorp Market
Norfolk NR11 8TZ
ENGLAND
Phone: 0263-834823
Fax: 0263-834939
Heliscene Magazine

High Point Products Company
3013 Mary Kay Lane
Glenview, IL 60025
Phone: 312-272-8684
High Point balancers

Hobbico
P.O. Box 543
Champaign, IL 61824
Phone: 217-398-3630
Fax: 217-398-0008
Kyosho Concept helicopters and accessories

Hobby Dynamics Distributors
P.O. Box 3726
Champaign, IL 61826-6326
Phone: 217-355-0022
Fax: 217-355-0058
Kalt helicopters and JR radios

Hobby Lobby International, Inc.
P.O. Box 1285
Brentwood, TN 37027
Phone: 615-377-6948
MFA Sport 500 helicopter

Hobbypoxy/Petit Paint Co., Inc.
36 Pine Street
Rockaway, NJ 07886
Hobby Poxy paint

Hyatt Hobbies
45 Marchwood Road
Exton, PA 19341
Phone: 215-524-7244
Helicopter-related products

International Radio Controlled Helicopter Association (IRCHA)
6225 Taylorsville Rd.
Dayton, OH 45425
Phone: 513-236-8853

K&B Manufacturing Inc.
12152 Woodruff Ave.
Downey, CA 90241
*Super Poxy paints, K&B fuels
and engines*

Lenco Hobbies
819 Washington Street
Peekskill, NY 10566
Phone: 914-737-2999
Helicopter-related products

**Lightning Products; Div.
S.M.C.**
P.O. Box 1607
Tomball, TX 77377-1607
Rotor Craft work station

Mark's Helicopter Services
4913 Marcy Road
Dayton, OH 45449
Phone: 513-299-2384
*Hi Products composite rotor
blades*

Matrix Enterprises Inc.
7015 Carroll Road
San Diego, CA 92121-2212
Phone: 619-450-9509
*Space Case transmitter carrying
case*

McDaniel R/C, Inc.
12206 Guinevere Rd.
Glenn Dale, MD 20769
Phone: 301-464-2260
*Ni-Starter and remote glow plug
connectors*

Miniature Aircraft USA
2324 North Orange Blossom Trail
Orlando, FL 32804
Phone: 407-422-1531
Fax: 407-648-8609
*X-Cell helicopters and other heli-
copter-related products*

**Model Airplane News/Air
Age, Inc.**
251 Danbury Road
Wilton, CT 06897
Phone: 203-834-2900
Fax: 203-762-9803
Model Airplane News Magazine

Model Helicopter World
Traplet House, Severn Drive
Upton-upon-Severn
Worcestershire WR8 0JL
ENGLAND
Phone: 44-6846-4505
*Model Helicopter World Maga-
zine*

Morgan Fuels
P.O. Box 1201
Enterprise, AL 36331
Phone: 205-347-3525
Cool Power fuel

R.C.M.B., Inc.
898 West 16th Street
Newport Beach, CA 92663
Phone: 714-645-8830
Model Builder Magazine

R/C Helicopters Unlimited
759 E. Brokaw Rd.
San Jose, CA 95112
Phone: 408-436-1025
Helicopter-related products

R/C Modeler Corporation
144 West Sierra Madre Boulevard
Sierra Madre, CA 91024
Phone: 818-355-1476
Fax: 818-355-6415
RCM Magazine

R/C Models, U.S.A.
P.O. Box 6026
San Pedro, CA 90734
Phone: 213-833-4700
Morley helicopters

Radio Helicopter/Ashdown Publishers
Shelley House, 104 High Street
Steyning
West Sussex BN4 3RD
ENGLAND
Phone: 903-815599
Fax: 903-815599
Radio Helicopter-USA Magazine

Rave's Manufacturing U.S.A.
2629 Edgewater Drive
Orlando, FL 32801
Phone: 407-649-8983
Fax: 407-649-8972
Helicopter-related accessories

RC Helicopter Training School
P.O. Box 727
Crescent City, FL 32122-0727
Mr. Ernie Huber
Helicopter flight training school

Robart
310 N. 5th Street
St. Charles, IL 60174
Phone: 312-584-7616
Loctite products; pitch gauges

Robbe Model Sport
180 Township Line Road
Belle Mead, NJ 08502
Phone: 201-359-2115
Fax: 201-359-1415
Schluter helicopters and other related products

SR Batteries
Box 287
Bellport, NY 11713
Phone: 516-286-0079
Battery packs

Sullivan Products
One North Haven Street
Baltimore, MD 21224
Phone: 301-732-3500
Starters and other helicopter products

S & W Hobby Supply Co.
P.O. Box 208
Tatamy, PA 18085
Phone: 215-252-2024
S & W Fuels

Tech Specialties
218 Vernon Rd.
Greenville, PA 16125
Phone: 412-588-1335
Fax: 412-588-1571
Helicopter accessories

Yale Hobby Manufacturing Co. Inc.
3896 Selvitz Rd.
Ft. Pierce, FL 34981
Phone: 407-466-8883
Helicopter-related products

Zenith Aviation Books
P.O. Box 1
Osceola, WI 54020
Phone: 715-294-3345
Helicopter-related books

Glossary

aileron control   Refers to the control that causes an airplane to bank to either side; used interchangeably with the helicopter term *lateral cyclic*.

autorotation   The process or ability of a helicopter to safely descend and land without any assistance from the engine. The helicopter is required to have an autorotation clutch, which allows the blades to continue spinning when the engine stops. Collective pitch control is also required.

collective pitch control   Changes the angle of attack (pitch) of both main rotor blades simultaneously; used to vary the amount of lift created by the helicopter, thereby causing it to climb or descend.

drive train   A term used to describe the various components that make the main rotor and tail rotor rotate; consists of the engine, gears, bearings, and shafts. Many different arrangements of these above components are possible, but all accomplish the same thing.

elevator control   Refers to the control that causes an airplane to raise or lower its nose, thus causing it to climb or descend; used interchangeably with the helicopter term *fore and aft cyclic*.

fixed pitch control   The angle of the main rotor blades are not adjustable in flight with this control system. To make the helicopter climb or descend, the speed of the rotor system is changed by varying the throttle position, changing the amount of lift produced. The fixed pitch control system reacts slower than the collective pitch control system, but it is also less complicated.

flybar   A part of most rotor head designs, it is the metal rod that is positioned perpendicular to the rotor blades in the same flight path. Flybar paddles are located at each end of the flybar. Through mechanical linkages, the flybar adds stability to the helicopter design and also amplifies the control inputs made by the pilot.

fore and aft cyclic control   The control that causes a helicopter to tilt front or back while hovering, or to climb and descend while in fast forward flight.

gyroscopic stabilizer (gyro)   A piece of electronic equipment used to help keep the helicopter headed in the correct direction. The gyroscopic stabilizer senses rotation of the model helicopter and sends a signal to the tail rotor servo to make the appropriate correction. The use of a gyro is so beneficial with RC helicopters that it is almost considered a necessity.

lateral cyclic control   The control that causes a helicopter to tilt to either side while hovering, or to bank through a turn while in fast forward flight.

main rotor   The helicopter is lifted and controlled in flight by the main rotor, which consists of the blades and all parts that support them. Typically, the main rotor has two blades, but as many as five are used on scale helicopters when the rotor head copies the original.

pod and boom helicopter   The most common type of model helicopter, both for learning and for sport flying. The radio equipment at the front of the model is covered by a plastic canopy—the pod—and the tail of the helicopter consists of a metal tube—the boom. This type of construction is less complicated than the full-fuselage style used on scale helicopters.

pushrod   A metal rod that connects one part of the helicopter control system to another. Typically at least one end of the rod is threaded to allow for adjustment.

receiver   Takes the radio signal from the transmitter, decodes it, and sends the individual control signals on to each servo.

rudder control   Refers to the control on an airplane that makes it yaw to either side; used interchangeably with the helicopter term *tail rotor control*.

runout   The amount of wobble that can be measured in a rotating part. The fan hub, clutch, and start shaft are the most common parts to check. A machinist's tool called a dial indicator is used to check the amount of runout.

scale helicopter   Term used to describe an RC helicopter that is modeled after an existing full-size helicopter. This type of model will have either a plastic or fiberglass shell, called the fuselage, that encloses the mechanics of the helicopter.

servo   A servo's function is to take the control information from the receiver and convert it into physical movement. Pushrods then pass this movement on to the controls on the model helicopter.

swashplate   The swashplate transfers controls from the nonrotating part of the helicopter to the spinning rotor head. It consists of two rings joined by a ball bearing, with control connections on each ring. Pushrods connected to the lower half can tilt the swashplate up to twenty degrees in any direction. The helicopter will move in whatever direction the swashplate is tilted.

tail rotor   To counteract the torque of the main rotor, a tail rotor is fitted to the helicopter. It is a smaller set of rotor blades mounted at the back of the helicopter, facing sideways. The blades are driven by the same engine as the main rotor. The angle of the tail rotor blades can be varied in flight to compensate for changes in the main rotor pitch, and also to cause the helicopter to rotate about its vertical axis.

tail rotor control   The control on a helicopter that is used to make it yaw, or rotate about its vertical axis; used to keep the helicopter aimed in the intended direction, this term is interchangeable with *rudder control*.

tracking   Refers to the flight path of each rotor blade, as compared to the other. The pitch (angle) of each rotor blade must be adjusted so that the blades follow exactly the same path through the air. You can check this by viewing the helicopter in flight from the side. The rotor blades should appear to form only one disk, rather than two.

transmitter   The part of the radio system that the helicopter flier holds in his hands. The transmitter takes control inputs from the pilot and sends them to the receiver in the helicopter.

yaw   To rotate around the vertical axis. On a helicopter, yaw is controlled by the pitch of the tail rotor blades.

Index